OFSTED REVIEWS OF RESEARCH

TANDARDS
TION

Recent Research in Mathematics Education 5 – 16

Askew
Wiliam
EDUCATION
COLLEGE
IDON

ISBN 0 11 350049 1

Office for Standards in Education
Alexandra House
29–33 Kingsway
London WC2B 6SE

Telephone 0171-421 6800

CONTENTS

Foreword v

Acknowledgements vi

Introduction 1

The international context 4
High scores in school mathematics at age 14 are associated with the presence of what might be termed a 'mathematical ethos' in schools.

Young children's competency with number is often underestimated 6
There is a strong link between children's strategic use of counting and their understanding of numerals.

'Knowing by heart' and 'figuring out' support each other in pupils' progression in number 8
To accept without question primitive methods [eg counting for addition] used by lower- attaining children, ensures the divide between them and their higher-attaining peers will grow even wider.

Moving from practical to formal work is often far from straightforward 10
Practical work can provide images that help pupils contextualise mathematical ideas. It can also provide experiences out of which pupils can abstract mathematics. But research shows that these transitions are not always smooth. Pupils have difficulty in contextualising formal mathematics and the ideas that they abstract from practical work may not be the ones the teacher intended.

Learning is more effective when common misconceptions are addressed, exposed and discussed in teaching 12
We have to accept that pupils will make some generalisations that are not correct and many of these misconceptions remain hidden unless the teacher makes specific efforts to uncover them.

Careful choice of examples improves children's concept formation 14
The ideal examples to use in teaching are those that are 'only just' examples, and the ideal non-examples are those that are very nearly examples.

Effective questioning can raise achievement 16
Although the use of extended 'wait-time' for higher-level questions can increase pupil achievement, questions may not always be the most effective way to generate discussion.

The quality of praise is at least as important as its quantity 18
When praise is used infrequently, given uncritically and without enthusiasm, and expressed in very general terms, then it is at best ineffective and, at worst, can have damaging consequences for pupil learning.

Pupils learn more when their teachers know their attainment and can act on this information 20
A study of infant teachers found that the more teachers knew about their pupils' mathematical knowledge, the better the pupils were at word-problem-solving. Knowledgeable teachers questioned their pupils about problem-solving processes and listened to their responses, while less knowledgeable teachers tended to explain problem-solving processes to pupils or just observe their pupils' solutions.

Pupils need to be introduced to a wide range of problem-solving situations 22
Computational skills can be introduced through problem-solving.
This requires teachers to observe and assess how pupils solve problems as well as whether they solve them correctly.

Success in problem-solving requires both specific content knowledge and general skills 24
Just as competence in early number relies on a blend of 'knowing that' and 'figuring out', improving competence at mathematical problem-solving involves increasing and developing together both the fund of mathematical knowledge and a range of general strategies.

What mathematics is learnt is closely tied to the circumstances in which it is learnt 26
Pupils' success in school mathematics may depend on their knowledge of how classrooms operate as much as their mathematical understanding.

Pupils' self-confidence and beliefs affect their success in mathematics 28
One of the most important things that a teacher can do is to foster a view of ability in mathematics as changeable rather than fixed.

Calculators can improve both performance and attitude 30
Open access to calculators does not lead to dependence on calculators, and can improve pupils' numeracy.

The differences between girls' and boys' attainment in mathematics are small and narrowing 32
An analysis of 98 studies of the differences in mathematics achievement between males and females shows that the average difference is very small, and has been decreasing steadily.

Computers can have a substantial positive impact on pupil's achievement in mathematics 34
Using a computer to teach particular topics results in more rapid learning for pupils, and higher levels of achievement.

Co-operative small group work has positive effects on pupil achievement 36
The benefits of co-operative learning activities hold for pupils at all age levels, for all subject areas, and for a wide range of tasks, such as those involving rote-decoding, retention, and memory skills, as well as problem-solving ability.

The benefits of small group work depend on the type of grouping 38
The benefits of small group work appear to be most marked when there is an appreciable, but not the full, range of abilities in the group. In mixed-sex groups, the achievement of males and females is most similar when there is an equal number of males and females.

Mathematical attainment grouping can lead to some gains in attainment 40
Contrary to popular belief, setting does not appear to lead necessarily to low self-esteem for low-attainers. It would appear that seeing someone of similar attainment cope is more motivating than seeing mastery.

Many aspects of mathematics teaching are under-researched 42

Notes 45

FOREWORD

OFSTED has commissioned a limited number of brief but authoritative reviews of research aimed principally to support teachers and those in training to be teachers. Each review will focus on a key topic of general concern. In that achievements in literacy and numeracy are fundamental to all other learning, I am very pleased to welcome the first of these reviews, *Mathematics Education 5-16*, prepared by Mike Askew and Dylan Wiliam of King's College, London.

I am sure that both primary and secondary teachers - and not just mathematics specialists - will find the review thought-provoking. I hope that the review raises awareness of mathematics research and promotes discussion among teachers, enabling them to look at their practice with a fresh eye.

Chris Woodhead
Her Majesty's Chief Inspector of Schools

Acknowledgements

We would like to thank Kath Cross HMI and Angela Walsh for their support and guidance throughout the compilation of this review.

We are also grateful to the numerous teachers who read and commented on various drafts of the review as it was produced. Their comments have been invaluable in shaping its final form.

Finally, we would like to thank Mundher Adhami, Alan Bell, Jo Boaler, Margaret Brown, Leone Burton, Susan Cameron, Lynn Churchman, Gill Close, Geoffrey Howson, Barbara Jaworski, David Johnson, Mike McLachlan, George Smith and Sue Southwood for their helpful comments on earlier versions of the review, although, of course, none of these are responsible for any omissions or misrepresentations that remain. These are entirely the fault of the authors, each of whom would like to take this opportunity to state publicly that they are the fault of the other.

INTRODUCTION

As part of its work, in 1980, the Cockcroft Committee commissioned a review of existing research on the teaching and learning of mathematics, which was published in three volumes in 1983.

The aim of this booklet is to present, in as accessible a form as possible, subsequent research into effective mathematics teaching. In order to select amongst the thousands of articles and books that have been written during this period, we have chosen to concentrate on those studies that have been conducted in real classrooms, rather than in artificial 'laboratory' settings, and on those that have demonstrated significant impact on the quality of pupils' achievement in, or attitudes to, mathematics. Inevitably, this has entailed leaving out some well-conducted and valuable research, but, on the other hand, unless research can change what actually happens in classrooms, then it is of very little use to the busy classroom practitioner.

In order to ensure the quality of the research that we have selected, we have placed much more emphasis on research reported in journals which subject all articles submitted to a rigorous process of 'peer review' (often called 'refereed journals'). This does not mean that we consider research reported in other ways less valuable, but within the time available for the compilation of this review, there would not have been time for scrutiny of the research methods used.

Most of the research cited here has been conducted in the United States–it has been a sobering experience to realise how little British research there is on important issues in teaching and learning–but we have been careful only to select research that we believe may transfer to the British context. There are sometimes differences in terminology between the USA and Great Britain, and in reporting American studies, we have 'translated' the terms for the British reader. For example, in the USA, the term 'problem' is often used to denote a very narrow range of arithmetic word-problems, so where an American study uses the term 'problem-solving' with such a meaning, we have used the term 'word-problem-solving' to make clear that the term is being used in its narrower sense. Another example is the use of the word 'ability' where 'attainment' might be more appropriate. Where we have continued to refer to ability, this is not to be interpreted as representing a 'fixed' view of individual pupils' ability to achieve in mathematics.

In order to keep the review down to a reasonable size, we have chosen not to present separate reviews of research in different mathematical topics. Instead, we have emphasised those aspects of good mathematics teaching that appear to be common across a range of topics, although we have used particular examples to illustrate the points being made. For readers interested in the 'state-of-the-art' in the teaching of particular topics, excellent summaries are provided in the *Handbook of research on mathematics teaching and learning* edited by Douglas A Grouws. More accessible summaries of the way that research can be used to improve the teaching of specific topics are contained in three books in the *Research ideas for the classroom* series published by the National Council of Teachers of Mathematics in the USA.

One large area of research that is given less coverage here than the volume of research literature would indicate is the teaching of pupils with special educational needs. This is due to shortage of space–indeed, a review of this literature could form a booklet of this size by itself.

We did not envisage that a review such as this would be read from cover to cover, but would rather be 'dipped into' by teachers and others in order to find out what research says about particular aspects of teaching and learning mathematics. For this reason, we have tried to ensure that each double-page spread is as self-contained as possible, with significant references included at the foot of the page. These will provide a source of more detailed information for the interested reader. However, a complete list of all research cited on each page can be found at the end of the booklet.

Research

Grouws, D A (Ed.) (1992). *Handbook of research on mathematics teaching and learning.* New York, NY: Macmillan.

Jensen, R J (Ed.) (1993). *Research ideas for the classroom volume 1: early childhood mathematics.* New York, NY: Macmillan.

Owens, D T (Ed.) (1993). *Research ideas for the classroom volume 2: middle grades mathematics.* New York, NY: Macmillan.

Wilson, P T (Ed.) (1993). *Research ideas for the classroom volume 3: high school mathematics.* New York, NY: Macmillan.

The international context

High scores in school mathematics at age 14 are associated with the presence of what might be termed a 'mathematical ethos' in schools.

Since the publication of the last review of research in mathematics education, attention has been focused very sharply on the standards of mathematics achievement in this country by a series of comparisons with performance in other countries. The two most important of these were the second international mathematics study (SIMS), organised by the International Association for Educational Achievement (IEA), and the International Assessment of Educational Progress (IAEP). TIMSS, the third international mathematics and science study, is currently under way.

SIMS looked at the performance of two cohorts: 13-14-year-olds and 17-18-year-olds. At age 18, performance in England and Wales was high (ranked 3rd or 4th in most topics) although the proportion of the age cohort studying mathematics in England and Wales was lower than most other countries.

At age 14, mathematical performance in England and Wales was much more mixed. England and Wales was ranked only 13th out of 20 in number and measurement, and 14th in algebra, although it was ranked 5th in geometry, and 4th in descriptive statistics. This last fact is quite surprising when one considers that teachers in 15 out of the 20 countries considered the statistics items used in the tests to be more appropriate for their pupils than did teachers in England and Wales.

Interpreting these results, however, is difficult. For example, the tests developed for the international comparisons had to be appropriate for all 20 countries, and many items that would have reflected the greater breadth of the mathematics curriculum in England and Wales could not be used. The cultural differences in terms both of schooling in general, and mathematics in particular, also compound the difficulties of comparison.

In all 20 countries, pupil performance in measurement, geometry and statistics was very close to teachers' predictions based on the syllabus studied. However, in number and algebra, in almost all countries, pupil performance fell far short of teachers' expectations. There could be several explanations for this, but it would appear that in most of the countries teachers' expectations may be unrealistic under present conditions in these two topics. This suggests that in the teaching of number and algebra it is particularly important for teachers to evaluate carefully what students have learnt and understood before going on any further. There is also a suggestion that the comparative level of achievement in mathematics at age 9 is less good than it is at age 13, suggesting this area as a priority of future in-service education (as well as raising questions as to how and why pupils have caught up at 13).

More recently, many other comparative studies have been conducted, but none has come close to the IEA study in the care taken to match the samples of pupils selected. As a result general conclusions are hard to draw. Nevertheless, one conclusion that seems to emerge strongly is that high scores in school mathematics are associated with the presence of what might be termed a 'mathematical ethos' in schools, where mathematics is taught:

- for a large proportion of the school timetable all the way through to age 18;
- by well-qualified teachers;
- in longer (ie 60 minutes) rather than shorter lessons.

However, the countries with the highest achievement scores also have the most negative attitudes to the subject. Almost all of these countries make mathematics compulsory up to age 18, so that even where pupils dislike the subject, they need to carry on studying it to an advanced level in order to enter college or university. In England and Wales the study of mathematics beyond age 16 is not required for entry into higher education. Increased pressure on pupils to achieve well in mathematics up to age 16 might result in fewer pupils choosing to study mathematics beyond 16. The international comparisons data suggest that this could lead to a weakening of the 'mathematical ethos', and a consequent reduction in levels of pupil achievement.

RESEARCH

Burstein, L (Ed.) (1992). *The IEA study of mathematics III: pupil growth and classroom processes.* Oxford: Pergamon.

Lapointe, A E; Mead, N A & Askew, J M (1992). *Learning mathematics: report of the second International Assessment of Educational Progress.* Princeton, NJ: Educational Testing Service Center for the Assessment of Educational Progress.

Robitaille, D. F., & Garden, R. A. (Eds). (1988). *The IEA study of mathematics II: contexts and outcomes of school mathematics.* Oxford: Pergamon.

Travers, K J & Westbury, I (Eds.). (1989). *The IEA study of mathematics I: analysis of mathematics curricula.* Oxford: Pergamon.

Young children's competency with number is often underestimated

There is a strong link between children's strategic use of counting and their understanding of numerals.

In recent years research attention has begun to focus on the understanding of number that young children bring to school. This represents a shift towards examining what young children can do rather than focusing on what they cannot do, or assuming that they bring no mathematical knowledge with them when they start school.

Before beginning formal schooling, many young children can:

- count meaningfully
- use terms like 'more' and 'less' appropriately
- have some understanding of addition and subtraction with small numbers
- invent strategies for solving problems.

While children can display such competences, it is also apparent that their understandings of the purposes behind skills like counting do not always accord with how adults perceive the task. Detailed interviews with Scottish nursery pupils at three times in the year revealed an understanding of counting as something you 'just do', rather than to find out the quantity. Asked what was counted at home, one child was surprised at the question, replying 'But counting's just saying the words!' Pupils also commonly confused counting with 'reading numerals', indicating that 'reading the clock' was included in what they considered to be counting.

While 'learning the words' is clearly important, it is only a part of what is involved in learning to count. For example, when asked for a specific number of bricks, some children who could recite the number sequence quite adequately, would simply grab a quantity of bricks. A major task of the teacher would therefore seem to be to help pupils come to a view of counting as a purposeful activity.

Over the year of the Scottish research project, many children shifted from grabbing to counting, indicating that they had begun to relate the number sequence to the operation of counting. For some children, representing four by writing 1 2 3 4 appeared to act as a link between the verbal and written number systems.

This study also confirmed other research findings that pupils have particular difficulty with the 'teens', due to the idiosyncratic number names and the similarities with the multiples of ten (eg 'thirteen' and 'thirty'). Once the structure of the 'teens' has been learned, young children's verbal counting ability increases rapidly to 29 or 39, indicating a development of their understanding of the 'decade' system.

Another study of a small class of 'reception-aged' children provided a detailed picture of children's numerical knowledge at the start of the school year, again through detailed and extended interviews. A range of competences was revealed with the higher-attaining children well towards success on level 1 of the number attainment target in the National Curriculum. Even the lower-attaining children displayed a range of informal competences and some conventional knowledge, but this tended to be less stable. The overall impression was that, while perhaps not knowing the standard ways of representing numbers, children already possess some mathematical competences by the time they enter 'Reception' classes.

However, such studies have tended to concentrate on mathematical content knowledge, with little attention to children's ability to solve problems through choosing and using appropriate mathematics. Competence involves not just the knowing of content, but also its application.

RESEARCH

Aubrey, C. (1994). An investigation of the mathematical knowledge and competencies which young children bring into school. *British Educational Research Journal,* 19(1) 27-41.

Munn, P. (1994). The early development of literacy and numeracy skills. *European Early Childhood Education Research Journal,* 2(1) 5-18.

'Knowing by heart' and 'figuring out' support each other in pupils' progression in number

To accept without question primitive methods [eg counting for addition] used by lower-attaining children, ensures the divide between them and their higher-attaining peers will grow even wider.

There is strong evidence in the research that, across all years of schooling, some pupils do not progress far beyond developing arithmetic techniques that rely on simple addition skills, such as 'counting on' or relying on repeated addition for multiplication.

A study of arithmetical methods used by 7- to 12- year-olds demonstrated that higher-attaining pupils had a range of alternative strategies to draw on, based on both:

- *'knowing by heart'– recall of some number facts*

  for example 5 + 5 = 10
- *'figuring out'– deriving or deducing other number facts on the basis of the known facts*

  for example 5 + 6 must be one more than 5 + 5.

On the other hand, lower-attaining pupils relied mainly on counting strategies based on objects (fingers or counters) or representations of objects.

These findings are supported by another study of pupils' arithmetic which identified approaches based either on figuring out or memorised procedures. Pupils who derived or deduced solutions rather than trying to recall taught procedures were more able to adapt their methods to cope with new problems and anticipate solution strategies.

It seems then that pupils with access to *both* recalled and deduced number facts make more progress because each approach supports the other:

- *deducing number facts helped pupils commit more facts to memory, and*
- *recalled facts helped expand the range of strategies for deriving facts.*

For some lower-attaining pupils it may be that over-dependence on counting methods, while leading (eventually!) to a correct result, removes the need to commit number facts to memory, which in turn limits their development of deductive approaches.

RESEARCH

Gray, E.M. (1991). An analysis of diverging approaches to simple arithmetic: preference and its consequences. *Educational Studies in Mathematics,* **22**(6) 551-574.

Hart, K. (Ed.) (1981). *Children's Understanding of Mathematics: 11-16.* London: John Murray.

Steffe, L.P. (1983). Children's algorithms as schemes. *Educational Studies in Mathematics,* **14** 109-125.

Moving from practical to formal work is often far from straightforward

Practical work can provide images that help pupils contextualise mathematical ideas. It can also provide experiences out of which pupils can abstract mathematics. But research shows that these transitions are not always smooth. Pupils have difficulty in contextualising formal mathematics and the ideas that they abstract from practical work may not be the ones the teacher intended.

Research demonstrates that from an early age children can operate with small numbers when they are linked to objects (eg two elephants and two more elephants). But even after immediately being 'tuned in' to the real-world/mathematics link, they find it difficult spontaneously to put into a context numbers presented in an abstract form. For example, one way of working out the answer to '2+2' is to translate this spontaneously into 'two elephants and two more elephants'. Furthermore, there is little evidence to suggest that facility in putting ideas into context gets any better with age.

The Children's Mathematical Frameworks project confirmed that the link between practical work and the move to formal symbolic mathematics is often tenuous. Groups of six pupils across the attainment range were individually interviewed on four occasions: prior to a topic being taught, immediately before the move from the practical to the more formal aspects of the topic (eg formal algorithms, symbolisation), immediately after the introduction of the formal aspects and three months later. Across several topic areas (subtraction, fractions, areas, volumes, equations and ratio), amongst pupils spanning the ages eight to thirteen, a consistent pattern was found:

> Approximately one-third of the pupils had some access to the formal mathematics even before the teaching began, one-third did not acquire the formal aspects, and the remaining third learnt the formal aspect with varying degrees of success.

For those pupils who already had access to the formal mathematics, the time spent on practical work, from which they were expected to abstract the ideas, was probably unnecessary. The time might have better been used for these pupils to explore the justification of the result.

The third of pupils who made little or no progress in the formal seemed either:

- to lack the necessary prerequisite skills or understanding to appreciate the new ideas (for example, errors in finding areas were a consequence of lack of skill in carrying out linear measurement); or
- to adhere to pre-existing misconceptions or 'intuitive' methods (for example, firmly believing that subtracting a larger number from a smaller number results in zero, leading to no appreciation of the need to decompose in subtraction).

Even the third of pupils who demonstrated some degree of success had difficulties. Probing in subsequent interviews revealed that there were still some misunderstandings which prevented short-term success from developing into longer-term understanding – for example, believing that the striking out of figures when subtracting by decomposition resulted in the total number changing.

Similarly, a detailed study and analysis of a group of pupils learning place value from tens and units blocks indicated that the blocks themselves served only as a vehicle for teacher talk–the learning came about from the way the teacher talked about and handled the blocks, rather than through the pupils' own discoveries.

The main message from such research is that while practical work and 'real' contexts can be useful, they need to be chosen carefully, and accompanied by careful dialogue with pupils to establish the extent of their understanding. Pupils' success on a concrete task should not be taken as an indication of understanding the abstract. Practical and abstract each need to be explored in their own right. How links are perceived between the two needs to be the subject of considerable discussion between pupils and teachers.

However, the research also shows that this is far easier to say than to do. Setting time aside for dialogue is itself difficult enough (although asking pupils to write about what they have learnt can provide very revealing insights). Even when time is available, research suggests that it is easy to 'foreclose' on pupils–to jump to conclusions about a pupil's difficulty, either on the basis of limited information:

given 42 - 25 and asking what needs to be borrowed, assuming that the response 3 is simply the result of forgetting the rule rather than a 'sensible' answer

or by drawing on past experience

for example, assuming that one pupil's difficulty must be the same as one demonstrated by another pupil previously.

RESEARCH

Hughes, M (1986). *Children and number: difficulties in learning mathematics.* Oxford: Basil Blackwell.

Johnson, D C (Ed.) (1989). *Children's mathematical frameworks 8-13: a study of classroom teaching.* Windsor: NFER-Nelson.

Learning is more effective when common misconceptions are addressed, exposed and discussed in teaching

We have to accept that pupils will make some generalisations that are not correct and many of these misconceptions remain hidden unless the teacher makes specific efforts to uncover them.

One of the most important findings of mathematics education research carried out in Britain over the last twenty years has been that all pupils constantly 'invent' rules to explain the patterns that they see around them. For example, it is well known that many pupils quite quickly acquire the 'rule' that to multiply by ten one adds a zero. Pupils then often 'over-generalise' their rules to situations that do not work. In the case of multiplying by ten, they apply it to decimals (eg 2.3 x 10 = 2.30). Similarly, pupils may decide that multiplication always makes bigger, division smaller and then choose erroneously to multiply or divide according to their perception of whether the numbers need to get bigger or smaller.

However, overcoming these kinds of misconceptions presents the teacher with a dilemma. When teaching multiplying whole numbers by ten, in order to present pupils with examples where adding a zero does not work, it would be necessary to stray far from the original topic, and it may involve mathematical ideas that are, for the time being, beyond the pupils' capacity to understand.

A similar difficulty arises when teaching new procedures, where the most common approach is to apply the procedure first to simple examples and later to more complex examples. This can be counter-productive, since pupils often solve simple examples intuitively, without knowing how they have solved them, and such methods cannot be used with more complex examples. So, for example, when teaching pupils about methods for solving equations it may be better to start with examples that cannot be solved by intuitive methods such as just 'spotting' the solution or 'trial and error'.

The model of simple through to more complex examples can also lay the foundations of misconceptions. For example, teaching subtraction of tens and units and beginning with examples where no decomposition or carrying is required may reinforce the idea that you always take the smaller digit away from the larger, leading to later errors like 43 - 28 = 25.

It seems that to teach in a way that avoids pupils creating *any* misconceptions (sometimes called 'faultless communication') is not possible, and that we have to accept that pupils will make some generalisations that are not correct and many of these misconceptions will remain hidden unless the teacher makes specific efforts to uncover them. A style of teaching that constantly exposes and discusses misconceptions is needed, thus limiting the extent of misconceptions. This may be possible, as much research over the last twenty years has shown that the vast majority of pupil misconceptions are quite widely shared.

In the Diagnostic Teaching project, conducted at Nottingham University's Shell Centre for Mathematical Education, teaching packages were designed to elicit and address pupils' misconceptions in mathematics during lessons. Two important features emerged. The first was that addressing misconceptions during teaching does actually improve achievement and long-term retention of mathematical skills and concepts. Drawing attention to a misconception before giving the examples was less effective than letting the pupils fall into the 'trap' and then having the discussion.

The other major finding was that the *intensity* and degree of *engagement* with the task that pupils showed in group discussions were much more important influences on their learning than the amount of *time* spent on the task. Although the intensive discussions meant spending much longer on apparently small (though important) points, there was a much higher level of long-term retention overall than with classes that covered more ground superficially but in the same time.

RESEARCH

Bell, A W (1984). Structures, contexts and learning. *Journal of Structural Learning*, **8**(2), 165-171.

Bell, A W (1993). Some experiments in diagnostic teaching. *Educational Studies in Mathematics*, **24**(1), 115-137.

Fischbein, E; Deri, M; Nello, M S & Marino, M S (1985). The role of implicit models in solving verbal problems in multiplication and division. *Journal for Research in Mathematics Education*, **16**(1), 3-17.

Hart, K M (Ed.) (1981). *Children's understanding of mathematics: 11-16.* London: John Murray.

Careful choice of examples improves children's concept formation

The ideal examples to use in teaching are those that are 'only just' examples, and the ideal non-examples are those that are very nearly examples.

Research on concept formation shows that children make generalisations quite quickly wherever they recognise common patterns. What is less clear is the best way to help pupils form concepts most effectively. Forming a concept such as that of a 'triangle' has two aspects. Pupils need to learn both what are not examples of triangles (such as quadrilaterals, pentagons, shapes with curved sides, etc) and what *are* triangles.

For example, it is well known that many pupils believe that triangles are three-sided shapes *with the lowest side horizontal* (Figure 1). A triangle such as in Figure 2 is described by many pupils as "an upside-down triangle". They have learnt to rule *out* certain shapes (eg quadrilaterals and pentagons) but they have not learnt to rule *in* 'upside-down triangles'. This is because an *irrelevant* feature (in this case the orientation) is a common feature of most textbooks' treatment of triangles. Since most of the triangles that pupils see are oriented as in Figure 1, the notion of orientation becomes bound up with that of shape.

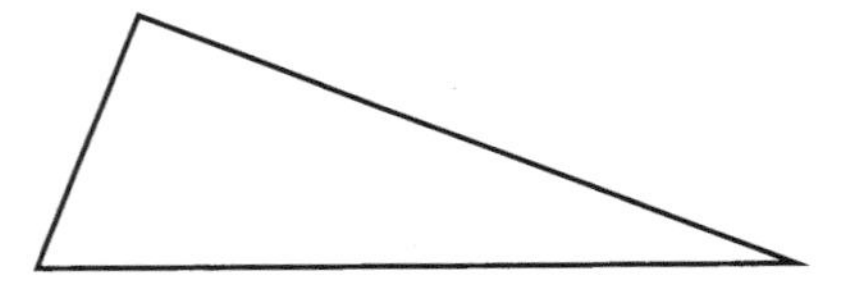

Figure 1: 'triangle'

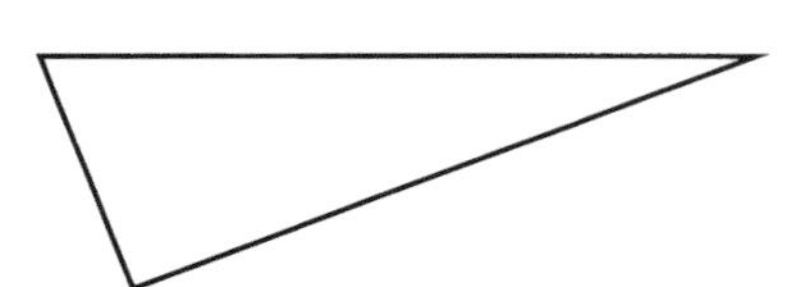

Figure 2: 'upside-down triangle'

Experiments conducted in psychological laboratories appear to have shown that 'ruling in' is more important than 'ruling out'. This would suggest that the best way to teach the concept of 'triangle' is to present pupils with lots of examples of triangles, rather than giving pupils a mixture of examples (ruling in) and non-examples (ruling out).

However, researchers in mathematics classrooms have produced very different findings. In particular they have found that sequences of examples and non-examples are more effective in teaching mathematics concepts than sequences of examples alone. The explanation for the differences between these two sets of research may lie in how commonly the examples used incorporate *irrelevant* features.

In the psychological studies, it appears that presenting sequences of examples that included consistent irrelevant features was rare, and so the irrelevant features did not get 'bound up' with the defining features. However, in typical classroom contexts, irrelevant features are common in the examples presented. Putting these ideas together (since it seems that 'irrelevant' features are common in most mathematical learning tasks), it is likely that pupils will still incorporate these 'irrelevant' features in their concepts and will make *under*-generalisations (ie they will not learn to 'rule in').

Therefore, in teaching concepts, teachers should use a mixture of examples and non-examples and should choose the examples so as to 'rule in' as much as possible, and should choose the non-examples to 'rule out' as much as possible. For example, if one wanted to teach pupils what a 'bird' was, it would be more helpful to say that a penguin is and a bat isn't, than to say that a robin is and an elephant isn't, in order to minimise the irrelevant features (in this example, wings) that are learnt along with the main concept.

Returning to the example of the triangle, we can think of a pupil's developing concept of a triangle in terms of a set diagram with non-triangles outside, triangles in their 'ordinary' or 'usual' positions clearly inside, and a kind of 'grey' area, including 'upside-down' triangles and obtuse-angled triangles (Figure 3). In order to minimise the 'grey' area, the ideal examples to use in teaching are those that are 'only just' examples (maximising what is 'ruled in'), and the ideal non-examples are those that are very nearly examples (maximising what is 'ruled out').

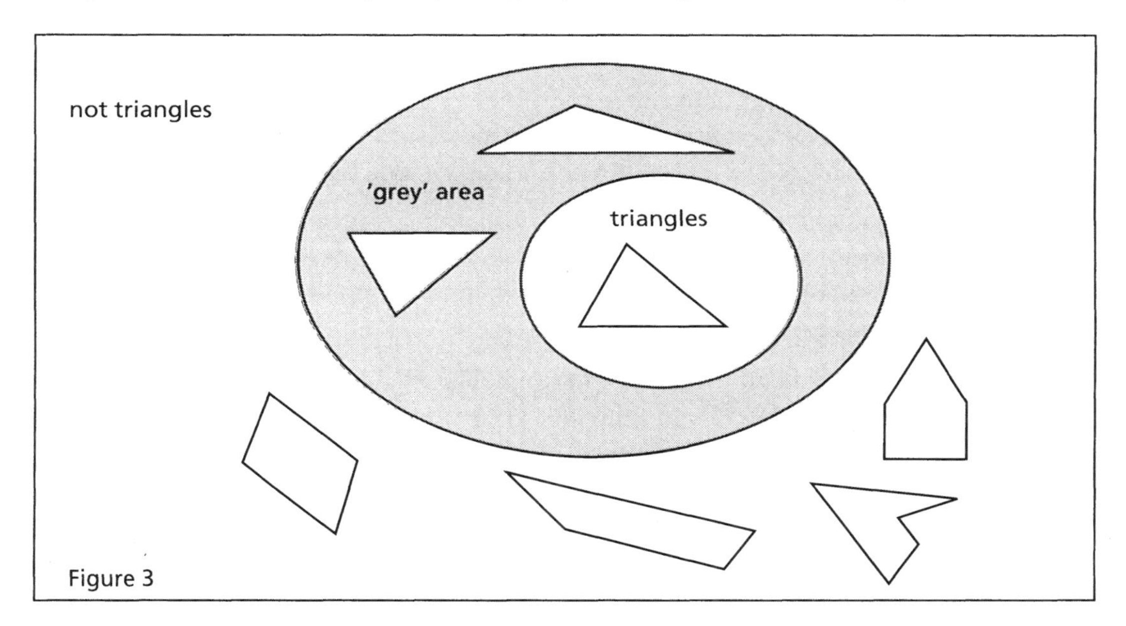

Figure 3

There is also evidence that rational sequencing (ie a sequence of examples, followed by a sequence of non-examples) is more effective in helping pupils to form concepts than random sequencing.

RESEARCH

Charles, R I (1980). Exemplification and characterisation moves in the teaching of geometry concepts. *Journal for Research in Mathematics Education,* **11(1), 10-21.**

Wilson, P S (1986). Feature frequency and the use of negative instances in a geometric task. *Journal for Research in Mathematics Education,* **17(2), 130-139.**

Effective questioning can raise achievement

Although the use of extended 'wait-time' for higher-level questions can increase pupil achievement, questions may not always be the most effective way to generate discussion.

Analyses of the kinds of questions that teachers ask in classrooms have shown that many teachers ask questions that test the ability of pupils to recall facts and procedures (often called *lower-level* questions), rather than the ability of pupils to apply, synthesise or explain their knowledge (often called *higher-level* questions).

For example, if we were to ask a pupil 'what is the name of this shape?', this would be a low-level question (recall). But if we were to ask 'how would you describe this shape to a friend over the telephone so that they could draw a copy?', then this would be a higher-level question (application). Again, questions such as 'give me all the pairs of numbers you can find which multiply to give 6' are of a higher order than simply asking for the answer to 3 x 2.

Although many inquiries have failed to find any relationship between the 'level' of questions and pupil achievement, many others have shown that pupils learn more in classrooms where teachers use a mix of both 'higher' and 'lower' level questions than in those in which teachers ask pupils mainly to recall or recognise.

By itself, such an association does not, of course, establish that higher attainment was *caused* by the style of questioning. However, many studies have shown that teachers can increase the proportion of higher-level questions that they use, and that such changes are accompanied by significant improvements in pupil performance. Further, these effects are more pronounced for understanding *concepts* and *principles* than for simple *recall* of facts.

Moreover, the average differences in achievement of those classes whose teachers used more demanding questioning were, in some cases, quite large–equivalent to as much as one year's learning.

Another significant aspect of a teacher's questioning style is the time the teacher pauses after asking a question, before either supplying the answer or a hint themselves, or moving on to a different pupil–often called 'wait-time'.

It is known that many teachers use average wait-times of less than one second, and many studies have shown that increasing 'wait-time' up to about three seconds significantly improves the achievement and attitudes of pupils, although other studies suggest that increasing wait-time is only beneficial for higher-level questions. This is not particularly surprising, since if a pupil cannot recall an answer, giving more time is unlikely to help!

However, what is rather surprising is that some studies have shown that waiting too long can *decrease* the quality of the teacher and pupil talk, with consequent *reduction* in pupil achievement in mathematics.

The 'best-evidence' conclusion appears to be that teachers should use a balance of low- and high-level questions in their teaching, with wait-times of at least three seconds for 'higher-level' questions.

Having said all this, although the use of extended wait-time for higher-level questions can increase pupil achievement, some questions, whatever their level, are less effective at generating discussion than provocative statements. Work by James Dillon has suggested that when teachers make *statements* in order to provoke discussion rather than ask questions, pupils can display more complex thought, deeper personal involvement, wider participation, greater interconnectedness, and richer inquiry. So for example, rather than asking "Are all squares parallelograms?", it might be more profitable to ask pupils to discuss the statement "All squares are parallelograms".

It seems important, therefore, to examine the range of things pupils are expected to respond to, and to vary the kinds of response open to pupils, from low-level questions, to high-level questions, and statements provoking discussion. Effective teaching will need to include all three.

RESEARCH

Dillon, J T (1985). Using questions to foil discussion. *Teaching and Teacher Education*, **1**(2), 109-121.

Redfield, D T & Rousseau, E W (1981). A meta-analysis of experimental research on teacher questioning behaviour. *Review of Educational Research*, **51**(2), 237-245.

Tobin, K (1986). Effects of teacher wait time on discourse characteristics in mathematics and language arts classes. *American Educational Research Journal*, **23**(2), 191-200.

The quality of praise is at least as important as its quantity

When praise is used infrequently, given uncritically and without enthusiasm, and expressed in very general terms, then it is at best ineffective and, at worst, can have damaging consequences for pupil learning.

There is a widespread belief amongst teachers and others involved in education that praise is a 'good thing'. However, there is no simple relationship between the use of praise and pupil achievement; many studies have found that teachers regarded as more effective than average actually used *less* praise than their less successful colleagues. Other features, such as the *quality* of the praise, and *what* is praised are at least as important, if not more so.

What appears to be most important for praise to be effective is that it is:

- contingent: the praise must depend on some particular thing the pupil has done, rather than the pupil's general performance.
- specific: the praise should identify the specific behaviour being praised, so that the pupil is aware of what aspect of their work is being singled out for praise.
- credible: the praise must be sincere; praise that follows a 'formula' (ie is always expressed in the same way) or which sounds insincere is likely to be ineffective, since pupils can 'see through' such praise very quickly.

Of course, the fact that particular kinds of praise are associated with enhanced pupil learning does not by itself prove that the praise is the cause of that improvement. However, the weight of evidence about the effects of different kinds of praise does suggest some guidelines which are shown opposite for the effective use of praise.

RESEARCH

Brophy, J (1981). Teacher praise: a functional analysis. *Review of Educational Research*, **51**(1), 5-32.

Dweck, C S (1986). Motivational processes affecting learning. *American Psychologist (Special Issue: Psychological science and education)*, **41**(10), 1040-1048.

Effective praise:	Ineffective praise:
is delivered contingently	is delivered randomly or unsystematically
specifies the particulars of the accomplishment	is restricted to global positive reactions
shows spontaneity, variety and other signs of credibility; suggests clear attention to the pupil's accomplishment	shows a bland uniformity, which suggest a conditioned response made with minimal attention
rewards attainment of specified performance criteria (which can include effort criteria)	rewards mere participation, without consideration of performance processes or outcomes
provides information to pupils about their competence or the value of their accomplishments	provides no information at all or gives pupils information about their status
orients pupils towards better appreciation of their own task-related behaviour and thinking about problem-solving	orients pupils towards comparing themselves with others and thinking about competing
uses pupils' own prior accomplishments as the context for describing present accomplishments	uses the accomplishments of peers as the context for describing present accomplishments
is given in recognition of noteworthy effort or success at difficult (for this pupil) tasks	is given without regard to the effort expended or the meaning of the task (for *this* pupil)
attributes success to effort and ability, implying that similar successes can be expected in the future	attributes success to ability alone, or to external factors such as luck or easy task
fosters endogenous attributes (pupils believe that they expend effort on the task because they enjoy the task and/or want to develop task-relevant skills)	fosters exogenous attributions (pupils believe that they expend effort on task for external reasons – to please the teacher, win a competition or reward etc.)
focuses pupils' attention on their own task-relevant behaviour	focuses pupils' attention on the teacher as an external authority figure who is manipulating them
fosters appreciation of and desirable attributions about task-relevant behaviour after the process is completed	intrudes into the ongoing process, distracting attention from task-relevant behaviour

From Brophy, J (1981). Teacher praise: a functional analysis. *Review of Educational Research,* **51**(1), 5-32.

Pupils learn more when their teachers know their attainment and can act on this information

A study of infant teachers found that the more teachers knew about their pupils' mathematical knowledge, the better the pupils were at word-problem-solving. Knowledgeable teachers questioned their pupils about problem-solving processes and listened to their responses, while less knowledgeable teachers tended to explain problem-solving processes to pupils or just observe their pupils' solutions.

There is little doubt that assessment exerts a strong influence on teachers and pupils. Assessments send clear messages about what is valued and can motivate pupils, although this can have both positive and negative consequences.

For example, in a regional initiative involving 52 French primary schools, clarifying the requirements for 'graduating' into the next class (by sending diagnostic assessment materials to all teachers) reduced the number of pupils failing to 'graduate' by 30%. On the other hand, much research in the USA has shown the negative effects that over-reliance on standardised achievement tests can have on the quality of teaching.

There is far less research, however, on the benefits of assessment carried out by classroom teachers as part of their normal teaching in order to find out what their pupils have learnt. Most of the research that has been carried out on teachers' classroom assessments has focused on the frequency of testing, and has looked at relatively 'low-level' skills such as recall of knowledge. This research indicates very clearly that regular classroom testing does increase these aspects of attainment in mathematics, although testing more frequently than once a month appears to have little additional effect. Whether such regular testing has any impact on 'higher-level' learning (either negative or positive), is not clear and the effect on long-term retention is not addressed.

What is clear from the research is that teachers' own overall judgements of their pupils' general levels of achievement correlate well with 'external' measures such as tests and examinations, although there are marked variations between teachers. Generally, teachers are better at judging the attainment of high-attainers than low-attainers, and are more accurate in judging pupils' scores on items that test computational skill than on those that test mathematical concepts.

However, knowing a pupil's general level of attainment is not much of a guide to whether they have specific competences, because of the complex way in which children's mathematical knowledge is built up. In a very important series of studies, Brenda Denvir found that it was possible to devise quite accurate 'maps' of the number concepts of low-attaining junior school pupils, and these were useful in directing teaching. The most surprising finding from the studies, though, was that what a pupil learnt was often quite different from what had been taught. For example, using the 'map' of number concepts, it was ascertained that a particular pupil's progress was being hampered because she had to 'work the answer to questions like '30 + 5', '43 + 10' and '25 - 10' out' rather than being able to answer immediately. After direct, but varied, teaching on these types of questions, the pupil appeared to have made no progress, although she had acquired several other new skills *not* directly taught. A few months later, she could answer immediately questions like 30 + 5, apparently without any further direct teaching on the topic, although questions like 43 + 10 and 25 - 10 were still beyond her. What was learnt was not the same as what was taught. Teachers therefore need to spend time finding out what has been learnt (diagnosis), and perhaps take appropriate action (remediation) before 'moving on'.

It is also clear that teachers can improve their diagnostic and remediation skills. In a recent study 40 infant teachers participated in a four-week workshop. Half were trained to diagnose and remedy the difficulties that their pupils experienced while solving word-problems and half were trained in strategies to keep pupils 'on-task' more. Those trained in diagnosis taught word-problem-solving significantly more and number facts significantly less than did the others. They also knew more about the processes that individual pupils used to solve problems, and their pupils did better in number knowledge, understanding, problem-solving and confidence.

In addition, the more teachers knew about their pupils' mathematical knowledge, the better the pupils were at word-problem-solving. Knowledgeable teachers questioned their pupils about problem-solving processes and listened to their responses, while less knowledgeable teachers tended to explain problem-solving processes to pupils or just observe their pupils' solutions.

However, knowing more about what pupils can and cannot do (diagnosis) does not in itself seem to lead to higher achievement–it is also necessary for teachers to be able to take appropriate action (remedy). For example, a study of upper-junior school teachers in Germany found that the lowest levels of achievement were found in classes where the teachers knew their pupils' attainment well, but had only a limited range of teaching approaches and were thus unable to act on this information. Levels of performance were higher in classes where teachers didn't know their pupils' attainment well, whether they had a wide range of teaching approaches or not. The highest levels of achievement were found in classes where teachers had a good knowledge of their pupils' achievement *and* a wide range of teaching approaches.

RESEARCH

Crooks, T J (1988). The impact of classroom evaluation practices on students. *Review of Educational Research,* **58**(4), 438-481.

Peterson, P L; Carpenter, T & Fennema, E (1989). Teachers' knowledge of students' knowledge in mathematics problem solving: correlational and case analyses. *Journal of Educational Psychology,* **81**(4), 558-569.

Pupils need to be introduced to a wide range of problem-solving situations

Computational skills can be introduced through problem-solving. This requires teachers to observe and assess how pupils solve problems as well as whether they solve them correctly.

There is a wealth of studies discussing the teaching and learning of problem-solving in school mathematics. Closer examination of the range of studies reveals a diversity of interpretations of what constitutes a problem. In some studies a problem is simply any question that requires the solver to select the mathematical operation, even if it is obvious which operation to use. Other studies define problems as situations presenting the problem solver with some sort of 'blockage' (i.e. that the appropriate mathematical action to take should not be immediately obvious to the problem-solver). This latter emphasis means that problems do not exist independently of the solver: what may be a problem for one pupil may not be for another.

Further distinctions are possible over the type of problem, and most classifications are broadly along the lines of:

- Standard problems: stories requiring translation into mathematical operations (also referred to as 'word-problems' or 'story-problems').
  Biscuits come in packs of 6. A carton holds 24 packs. How many biscuits are in the carton?
- Non-standard problems: situations for which the problem-solver will not have a set routine or procedure for finding a solution.
  There are 20 guests at a party. If everyone shakes hands with everyone else, how many handshakes will there be in total?
- 'Real world' problems: situations where the pupils will have to select the relevant information and set up a mathematical model that simplifies the situation.
  How can we improve the queuing system at dinner time?
- Puzzles: Problems depending upon luck, insight or unusual strategies for their solution.
  A square piece of cheese can be cut into 9 smaller squares with four cuts - two across and then two down. If the pieces are rearranged between cuts, can the 9 smaller squares be made with fewer cuts?

The bulk of research, particularly in the USA, has concentrated on standard problems. One review of research examined studies that looked at correlations between pupils' general abilities and problem-solving performance. Out of a total of 194 studies reviewed, 181 dealt with standard problems while only 13 had used non-standard problems. In the UK much work in curriculum development has concentrated on non-standard and real-life problems, but there is little research evidence which examines the sort of teaching strategies necessary to help develop problem-solving skills. Nor are there studies providing insight into the effect of such work on pupil attainment.

Standard problems tend to be associated with 'exercises' at the end of chapters, where pupils know that the operation to use is, say, multiplication because the chapter was all about multiplication. However there is substantial research evidence that demonstrates that treating standard problems as non-standard ones–not assuming that pupils will instantly spot which operation to use–can provide effective learning situations. One such study suggests that:

- Story problems can be used to introduce computational skills, rather than being used for practice.
- Teachers need to assess how pupils solve problems as well as whether they solve them correctly. This involves listening carefully to pupils' explanations.
- The relationships among concepts, skills and problem-solving need to be stressed.

All this requires pupils to be introduced to a range of standard problems. Different mathematical operations and procedures can give rise to a range of situations. For example, addition and subtraction situations can be classified into four types: join, separate, part-part-whole and compare.

Join problems involve the adding of elements to a given set.

Separate problems, like join ones, involve action, but by the removal of items.

Part-part-whole and *compare* problems are those involving comparisons between two sets.

A further distinction is given by which quantity is unknown: the initial quantity (start unknown), the second quantity (change unknown) or the final quantity (result unknown). Bearing this in mind, simple situations can then provide a range of story problems.

- Five people are on a bus and 8 more get on. How many people are on the bus? (Join, result unknown)
- Some people are on a bus and 8 get off at a stop. Now there are 5 people on the bus. How many people were on the bus to start off with? (Separate, start unknown)
- Thirteen people are on a bus, five are children. How many are adults? (Part-part-whole)
- The first bus has 20 people on it, and the second 13 people. How many more people were on the first bus? (Compare)

RESEARCH

Hembree, R., Experiments and relational studies in problem solving: a meta-analysis. *Journal for Research in Mathematics Education, 1992.* **23**(3): p. 242-273.

Peterson, P.L., Fennema, E. and Carpenter, T.P. (1988/89), Using knowledge of how students think about mathematics. *Educational Leadership,* **46**(4) 42-46.

Success in problem-solving requires both specific content knowledge and general skills

Just as competence in early number relies on a blend of 'knowing that' and 'figuring out', improving competence at mathematical problem-solving involves increasing and developing together both the fund of mathematical knowledge and a range of general strategies.

Many comparisons of the way that high-attainers and low-attainers solve problems have shown clear differences in the way that they tackle problems.

A study of primary school pupils (aged from 4 to 9) looked at the strategies that pupils used when they were given a number of straight and curved pieces of railway track, and told that they had to make a complete loop so that the train could go all the way round the track without coming off.

Typically the younger pupils (ages 4 and 5) began arranging pieces of track immediately, joining them up more or less in the order in which they picked them up. In contrast, the older pupils spent a considerable time planning before beginning to arrange the pieces of track. It seems that the older pupils had a far clearer perception of the benefits of 'thinking about their thinking' (although it is not clear whether this ability continues to improve during secondary schooling). More generally, in all fields, experts spend more time than novices thinking about and finding a suitable representation for a problem, and getting a qualitative 'feeling' for the problem before beginning to work quantitatively. They also organise their knowledge around deep understanding of concepts and general principles while novices focus on surface details.

Successful problem-solvers seem to have a range of strategies that they use intensively in problem-solving, above and beyond the mathematical content that they know. These include checking that they have understood the problem, planning their approach, and monitoring their progress towards their goal.

Throughout the 1980s, there were many attempts to help pupils develop these kinds of strategies, so that they could apply them to novel and unfamiliar problems. However, by and large, such attempts have been unsuccessful. Attempting to teach general strategies 'in the abstract' appears to result in knowledge which is not applicable by the pupil.

Nevertheless 'thinking skill' approaches *have* been successful in improving performance in particular topic areas, particularly with low-attaining pupils, which suggests that thinking skills and subject knowledge develop hand in hand.

Learning is not only the constant build-up of new ideas but also the restructuring of old ones. The teaching of thinking or problem-solving skills is not distinct from, nor is it something to follow, the learning of the 'basics'. Just as competence in early number relies on a blend of 'knowing that' and 'figuring out', improving competence at mathematical problem-solving involves increasing both the fund of mathematical knowledge and a range of general strategies, which have to be developed together.

In the context of National Curriculum mathematics, this would suggest that learning activities which focus on separate attainment targets are less likely to be successful than those that require pupils to integrate ideas from two attainment targets (particularly where one of these is Ma1).

RESEARCH

Campione, J. C.; Brown, A. L. & Connell, M. L. (1988). Metacognition: on the importance of understanding what you are doing. In R. I. Charles & E. A. Silver (Eds.), *The teaching and assessing of mathematical problem solving* (pp. 93-114). Hillsdale, NJ: Lawrence Erlbaum Associates.

Nickerson, R. S. (1988). On improving thinking through instruction. In E. Z. Rothkopf (Ed.) *Review of research in education* (pp. 3-57). Washington, DC: American Educational Research Association.

Schoenfeld, A. H. (1992). Learning to think mathematically: problem solving, metacognition and sense making in mathematics. In D. A. Grouws (Ed.) *Handbook of research on mathematics teaching and learning* (pp. 334-370). New York, NY: Macmillan.

What mathematics is learnt is closely tied to the circumstances in which it is learnt

Pupils' success in school mathematics may depend on their knowledge of how classrooms operate as much as their mathematical understanding.

Research is beginning to raise questions about the nature of the separation of *what* is learned from *how* it is learned and *when* it is used. The activities through which knowledge is developed cannot easily be separated from the knowledge itself. For example, being able to 'do division' is clearly very different from knowing *when* to use division, and the context in which the learning takes place has an important impact on what is 'known'.

> *Children working in Brazilian street markets demonstrated a range of mathematical skills and knowledge which they had difficulty demonstrating in formal tests.*
>
> *A study of adults showed that they were unable to answer many questions presented as formal calculations that they had successfully carried out while shopping.*

Even when pupils succeed in classroom-based mathematical problem-solving, evidence suggests that they may draw on their understanding of the implicit rules that operate in classrooms, rather than just on how well they understand the mathematical structure of problems:

> *In word-problems found in textbooks, the relative sizes of the numbers can be a good indication of which operation to use (eg if the numbers are small, multiplication is more likely to be needed than addition).*
>
> *Spotting the key word: 'left' indicates subtraction and 'more' means addition*

Since problems in everyday life do not come in such neat forms, pupils whose learning depends on the use of such school-based cues will often be unable to apply their learning to 'real-world' situations. For such pupils, skill in real-world situations would then require the *learning* of a *new* set of ideas, rather than the *application* of *existing* ideas.

More generally, this evidence casts serious doubt on approaches to learning mathematics that are based on the assumption that pupils will be able easily to 'transfer' skills and knowledge learned in one context to others. Rather than trying to teach mathematical knowledge as isolated content, many researchers are now suggesting that attention needs to be paid to the concept being taught, the activity through which the concept is introduced and the 'culture' of the classroom. These three, concept, activity, and culture, need to be integrated; no one of the three can be understood independently of the other two. In particular, if pupils are to be able to apply the mathematics they know in novel situations then all three must be developed together.

This means that the activities used in classrooms need to mirror the sort of situations to which mathematics is actually applied (often called 'authentic' activities). The mathematical concepts should arise from the activities rather than being 'imposed' on them, and the teaching should emphasise that there is rarely a single 'right' method for solving a problem.

In promoting this integration of activity, concept and culture, it appears that emphasis needs to be placed on tasks that:

- are ill-defined (with irrelevant or insufficient information) and whose meaning needs to be negotiated;
- need to be carried out in a social setting, typically involving group-work; and
- have several possible solutions and solution methods.

RESEARCH

Brown, J S; Collins, A & Duguid, P (1989). Situated cognition and the culture of learning. *Educational Researcher*, **18**(1), 32-42.

Carraher, T N; Carraher, D W & Schliemann, A D (1990). Mathematics in the streets and in schools. In V. Lee (Ed.) *Children's Learning in School* (pp. 91-102). London, UK: Hodder & Stoughton in association with The Open University.

Lave, J (1988). *Cognition in practice: mind, mathematics and culture in everyday life.* Cambridge: Cambridge University Press.

Pupils' self-confidence and beliefs affect their success in mathematics

One of the most important things that a teacher can do is to foster a view of ability in mathematics as changeable rather than fixed.

The way that teachers praise and criticise pupils and their work has a significant impact on how pupils attribute their successes and failures. In recent years, this has led to the development of a strand of psychology called 'attribution theory'.

Pupils who view ability in mathematics as fixed tend to see their goal as gaining positive judgements (which would confirm that they are 'clever') and avoiding negative judgements on their performance (which would imply that they are 'no good' at mathematics). If they have confidence in their ability they will expect to be successful often and, in order to gain more positive confirmations of their ability, they will seek challenges and will show persistence in the face of difficulties (such an attitude is often described as 'mastery-oriented'). However, if they lack confidence in their ability, they will try to avoid challenges and show little persistence, because they believe that they are likely to fail and be 'shown up' (described as 'learned helplessness').

On the other hand, pupils who view ability in mathematics as changeable and incremental tend to have, as their goal, increasing their competence. Whether they are confident about their current ability or not, they will be 'mastery-oriented'. It therefore seems that one of the most important things that a teacher can do is to foster a view of ability in mathematics as *incremental* rather than *fixed*.

There is evidence in the research that the teacher can affect the way pupils attribute success or failure. For example, a study of five classes of seven-year-olds who were taught through problem-solving for a year compared the pupils' beliefs about learning mathematics with five matched classes who worked on a textbook-based scheme. Both groups were motivated to work hard and to understand, but the 'problem-solving' pupils were less inclined than the 'textbook' pupils to accept that conforming to particular methods (whether that of the teacher or of their peers) was the way to succeed. The 'problem-solving' pupils also believed more strongly that success arises out of trying to understand and explain one's thinking to others.

One year later the ten classes had been mixed up and the beliefs of the pupils about mathematics were investigated again. The formerly 'problem-solving' pupils still placed greater value on doing their best, being interested, attempting to understand and co-operate and developing personal methods of solution, but the gap in this last area between them and the 'textbook' pupils had narrowed. Furthermore, by this time both 'problem-solving' and 'textbook' pupils agreed on the need to conform to standard methods of solving problems, although this agreement was still stronger in the 'textbook' pupils.

More generally, there is a moderate correlation between self-confidence and achievement in mathematics, and, not surprisingly, those who are more confident of their ability to learn mathematics are more likely to continue studying mathematics when it becomes optional.

RESEARCH

Cobb, P., Yackel, E. and Wood, T. (1992). Interaction and learning in mathematics classroom situations. *Educational Studies in Mathematics,* **23**(1) 99-122.

Dweck, C S (1986). Motivational processes affecting learning. *American Psychologist*, **41**(10), 1040-1048.

Kloosterman, P., Self-confidence and motivation in mathematics. *Journal of Educational Psychology, 1988.* **80**(3), 345-351.

Calculators can improve both performance and attitude

Open access to calculators does not lead to dependence on calculators, and can improve pupils' numeracy.

Despite the lack of evidence to support the argument, there is still a feeling from some quarters that open access to calculators will lead to a reduction in basic arithmetical skills. One review examined 79 reports of investigations into calculator usage, all of which compared a group of pupils who were allowed access to calculators with a group that did not have in-class access. Pupil performance was measured on computation, concepts and problem-solving. The review concluded that access to calculators had a significant positive effect on average pupil performance, both on the use of paper and pencil algorithms and in tests of problem-solving, although very few of the studies followed up children for any length of time.

The only exception to this was with eight-and nine-year-old pupils. For this age, calculators appeared to detract from the growth of computational skills (based on seven studies).

An update of this review, drawing on data from a further nine studies, confirmed the positive benefits of access to calculators. The review also indicated that the use of the calculator during teaching can improve paper and pencil skills of pupils at all levels of attainment, although the gains were small.

As well as performance, the studies also provided information on pupils' attitudes. Those pupils with access to calculators had indicated a more positive attitude towards mathematics and a markedly better self-esteem in mathematics when compared to the pupils who had not had such access.

The Calculator Aware Number (CAN) Curriculum Project explored the effect of free access to calculators in, initially, twenty English and Welsh classrooms. The intention was for pupils to continue to have free access to calculators throughout their primary schooling, although formal algorithms would be taught by the teacher when appropriate. The evaluation of the project relied largely on case studies and provides insights into pupils' mathematical understanding when given free access to calculators. The amount of support provided for CAN teachers created favourable conditions, and its results may not therefore be easily generalisable. Nevertheless, teachers were particularly struck by the early age at which pupils became comfortable with very large numbers and began to operate with negative numbers.

In one local education authority, the use of a standardised mathematics test for eight-year-olds meant that the performance of CAN project pupils could be compared with that of other pupils of the same age. Altogether 116 project pupils were tested and their results compared with a group of the same size, selected randomly from a variety of non-CAN schools. The test covered a variety of aspects of mathematics, not just number. The results indicated that the CAN project pupils outperformed or matched the non-CAN pupils on the majority of test items.

- On 28 out of 36 items, project pupils outperformed non-project pupils. In 11 items the success rate of the project pupils was 10% or more higher, reaching 30% on one item.
- On the other 8 items, the non-project children performed as well or better, but the maximum difference in success was only just over 5% in favour of the non-project pupils.
- On 20 items, more project pupils attempted to answer than did non-project pupils, suggesting that the CAN pupils had a greater willingness to work independently.

These results have to be interpreted cautiously as it might be the case that the project pupils taking the test were not well matched to the pupils they were compared with. But, given the consistency and generality of the research findings, it seems reasonably safe to conclude that calculators are highly unlikely to harm mathematics achievement, and the priority must now be to develop new ways of exploiting the calculator as a tool for *teaching* number.

A more recent arrival, the graphical calculator, also appears to have considerable scope as a tool for teaching mathematics. Although early experiments focused on older pupils, recent work has shown that the use of graphical calculators can enhance both attainment and attitudes with lower-secondary pupils.

Considerable work still needs to be done to find the most effective ways in which these new tools can be used for teaching mathematics, and their long-term effects on pupils' mathematical development.

RESEARCH

Hembree, R. and Dessart, D.J. (1986). Effects of hand-held calculators in precollege mathematics education: a meta-analysis. *Journal for Research in Mathematics Education*, 17(2), 83-99.

Hembree, R. and Dessart, D.J. (1992). Research on calculators in mathematics education, in J.T. Fey and C.R. Hirsch (Eds.) *Calculators in mathematics education (1992 Yearbook* pp23-32). Reston, VA: National Council of Teachers of Mathematics.

Shuard, H.; Walsh, A.; Goodwin, J. & Worcester, V. (1991). *Calculators, children and mathematics: the calculator-aware number curriculum.* London, UK: Simon & Schuster.

The differences between girls' and boys' attainment in mathematics are small and narrowing

An analysis of 98 studies of the differences in mathematics achievement between males and females shows that the average difference is very small, and has been decreasing steadily.

In 1980, the Assessment of Performance Unit published the first two of a series of six reports on the mathematical performance of 11- and 15-year-old pupils in England and Wales.

The reports contained a wealth of interesting information (including pupils' performance in practical as well as written tests). However, for many, the most important finding was that while the achievement of girls and boys was comparable at age 11, the average scores for boys at 15 were higher than those for girls in all fifteen topics tested (significantly so in 12 of them). However, at the higher attainment ranges the discrepancy was even more marked. In the top 10% of pupils, the boys outnumbered the girls three to two.

Such results have always depended on the nature of the tests used. The format of the items, the contexts used, and the balance of topics all influence the relative performance of males and females. As a result, some subsequent studies have found more pronounced sex differences, while others have found almost none. Whatever the size of the differences, however, there was general agreement that the standard of achievement of girls in mathematics was cause for concern, and during the 1980s, a considerable amount of work was done to improve the performance of girls in mathematics.

Measured in any terms, these efforts have been remarkably successful. The 1992 pilot of National Curriculum tests for 14-year-olds showed that the average mathematical performance of girls is actually above that of boys (63% of girls achieved level 5 or higher, compared with only 60% of boys). Compared with the levels of achievement reported in the Cockcroft report for 1979, this improvement in girls' performance (relative to that of boys) corresponds to something like *an extra 6 months' mathematics learning.*

However, this improvement in the average attainment has not been matched by improvements for the highest attaining girls. In GCSE, girls account for 55% of the good grades (ie A-C) in English, but only 47% of the good grades in Mathematics, and at the highest levels (eg level 8 or above at age 14, grades A* at age 16) there are still only two girls to every three boys.

At A-level, while the number of girls doing either a Mathematics or Science A-level has increased slightly (from 71,300 in 1984 to 76,500 in 1993), the huge increase in the number of girls staying on to study A-levels (three times that of the boys) has largely occurred in non-mathematical subjects. While the proportion of boys and girls studying mathematics and science is now slightly more balanced than it was in 1984 (38.6% of students studying at least one mathematics or science A-level in 1984 were females, 41.4% in 1993), this has largely been as a result of a 'flight away' from mathematics and science by boys, rather than any increase of attractiveness of these subjects to girls.

Many reasons have been proposed for the remaining differences in attainment. At one extreme, it has been claimed that physiological differences between the brains of males and females might account for differential performance. Other explanations offered are that boys spend more time in early childhood playing with toys that develop spatial ability, or that girls are more disposed towards thinking styles that are less helpful in learning mathematics.

Whatever the arguments for and against these kinds of explanations, there is widespread agreement that they cannot alone explain the differences between the mathematical attainment of boys and girls and that other, more social, processes are involved.

In particular, it has become clear that the classroom experiences of girls, particularly in mathematics lessons, are very different from those of boys. These, together with other social influences, appear to account for the bulk of observed differences in achievement between girls and boys in mathematics. These issues are taken up in the following pages.

RESEARCH

Friedman, L (1989). Mathematics and the gender gap: a meta-analysis of recent studies on sex differences in mathematical tasks. *Review of Educational Research*, 59(2), 185-213.

McGuinness, D (1985). *When children don't learn: understanding the biology and psychology of learning disabilities.* New York, NY: Basic Books.

Stobart, G; Elwood, J & Quinlan, M (1992). Gender bias in examinations: how equal are the opportunities? *British Educational Research Journal*, **18**(3), 261-276.

Computers can have a substantial positive impact on pupils' achievement in mathematics

Using a computer to teach particular topics results in more rapid learning for pupils, and higher levels of achievement.

Although computers have been used in mathematics education in this country for well over twenty-five years, the pattern of usage is still very varied and very sparse. As a consequence the two strands of research into the effectiveness of computers–the classroom-based and 'laboratory'-based–have taken very different directions, asking different kinds of questions, and, not surprisingly, finding very different answers.

The classroom-based studies have shown that using a computer to teach particular topics and general reasoning skills results in more rapid learning for pupils, much more positive attitudes to subjects, and higher levels of achievement. These effects appear to be more marked for older pupils, and for low-attainers. However, perhaps surprisingly, the effects on pupils' attitudes to mathematics in the classroom-based studies are, at best, marginal, and there is little evidence to support the notion that teaching programming (eg using BASIC or Logo) improves general mathematical skills such as reasoning or problem-solving. It is also worth noting that even where use of computers has been more effective in improving learning than 'traditional' teaching, other innovative approaches, such as the use of paper- or card-based games have, in certain cases, been just as effective.

As well as using computers to 'take the place of the teacher' in the teaching of traditional mathematics content, the increased use of computers raises questions about the nature and content of the curriculum itself. There has been an increasing focus in mathematics education research on the way that computers can have an impact on which *aspects* of mathematics are emphasised, introduced or played down.

During the late 1980s, there was a swing away from using specifically *educational* computer applications for teaching particular parts of the curriculum, and towards the use of much more generic, content-free, software, such as spreadsheets and databases. However, more recently, it has been realised that software packages designed for commercial applications (for example business spreadsheets) have many features which are irrelevant to pupils, and some important aspects of their use are unhelpfully difficult. The balance therefore seems to be swinging back towards specifically *educational* software, but conceived in far broader terms than hitherto, ie generic software designed specifically for classroom use.

The crucial feature in evaluating educational software appears to be the tension between the extent to which the software *supports* and *constrains* the activity of the pupil. Using computers allows the teacher to create an environment for the pupil where the options open to the pupil are limited, so that the pupil is pushed into thinking about or using a particular aspect of mathematics (constraint). At the same time, the software allows the pupil to do things that would be difficult or impossible without the computer (support). A good example of this is 'BlockWorld' software which presents the pupil with a 'microworld' of Dienes place value blocks. At first sight, this might seem like a poor alternative to giving pupils (particularly younger ones) real wooden Dienes blocks to play with. However, the microworld forces the pupil to pay attention to particular features of the Dienes block system that are relevant for forming concepts of place value, in the same way that the teacher's talk does in small-group and individualised teaching.

Another effective example of innovative use of software is provided by the class of year 5 pupils who used the LogoWriter software to design learning software about fractions for use with year 4 pupils. By writing the software, the pupils learnt more about Logo and about fractions than either of two control groups, one of which had equivalent exposure to Logo, while the other followed its usual curriculum which included one lesson of Logo per week.

It is far too soon to provide any systematic evaluation of such innovations, but it currently seems likely that the most significant impact of computers on mathematics teaching will be on changing what is in the mathematics curriculum, as much as how it is taught.

However, one major concern over the use of information technology that has yet to be addressed in any significant way is that access to computers is not equitable. Pupils in economically disadvantaged areas, those from ethnic minorities, and females have less access to computers both at school and at home. Unless these issues of access are resolved, computers, despite their significant potential for remedying inequality, may serve only to re-inforce it.

RESEARCH

Bennett, P J (1991). Effectiveness of the computer in the teaching of secondary school mathematics: fifteen years of reviews of research. *Educational Technology*, **31**, 44-48.

Clements, D H (1987). Computers and young children: a review of research. *Young Children*, **43**(1), 34-44.

Kaput, J J (1992). Technology and mathematics education. In D. A. Grouws (Ed.) *Handbook of research on mathematics teaching and learning* (pp. 515-556). New York, NY: Macmillan.

Sutton, R E (1991). Equity and computers in the schools: a decade of research. *Review of Educational Research*, **61**(4), 475-503.

Watson, D M (Ed.) (1993). *The ImpacT report: an evaluation of the impact of information technology on children's achievements in primary and secondary schools.* London: King's College London Centre for Educational Studies.

Co-operative small group work has positive effects on pupil achievement

The benefits of co-operative learning activities hold for pupils at all age levels, for all subject areas, and for a wide range of tasks, such as those involving rote-decoding, retention, and memory skills, as well as problem-solving ability.

There is general consensus in research that at all ages:

- co-operative work has positive effects on pupil achievement, but
- such effects are dependent upon the existence of a shared goal for the group *and* individual accountability for the attainment of the goal.

These positive effects of co-operative work appear to be independent of pupil age, level of attainment, and type of school (urban, rural and suburban).

In addition to improving attainment, co-operative work also enhances self-esteem, inter-group relations, acceptance of pupils with special educational needs, attitudes towards school, and the skills of teamwork.

While the benefits of small group co-operative work are clear, the research does not suggest that this approach should be used to the exclusion of all others. Indeed, there is no universally agreed definition of what constitutes co-operative work, but there is agreement that group work does not 'just happen'.

Many studies have shown that pupils may be working *in* groups but not working *as* a group, and considerable skill is needed by the teacher to structure group work so that it is effective.

The research on co-operative learning can be grouped into two broad categories: co-operative problem-solving and peer tutoring.

Co-operative problem-solving

Learning together: Small, mixed-ability groups work collectively on the same task, but are trained and encouraged to help each other. The focus is on group processes, and a group reward can, but need not, be involved. Evidence suggests that this approach can enhance cognitive processing, peer support and encouragement, self-esteem and time on task.

Group-investigation: Pupils work in problem-solving, sometimes choosing topics and organising the work themselves. Work is evaluated by both pupils and the teacher. Such an approach appears to improve achievement, interpersonal behaviour between pupils, and attitude toward school.

Peer tutoring

Jigsaw: Working in small groups, material to be learnt is broken down into segments and each group member studies one segment. They meet with others working on the same segment to become 'experts' on that segment. Individuals then teach their aspect to other members of the original group. In comparison to whole-class teaching this approach improves liking of group, liking of school and self-esteem.

Pupil-team learning: The teacher presents material and then small mixed-ability groups prepare for tests. Team scores are based on pupils' scores on preceding tests, not through comparison with other pupils. The teams are ranked but individual contributions are also recognised, providing a mix of group rewards and individual accountability. This approach increases achievement and motivation, as well as producing positive relations and better 'social' behaviour.

There is no clear consensus in the research over the relative merits of group rewards and competition. In particular, the need for a group reward is questioned by some researchers. However, it may not be possible to have a co-operative task which has no element of group reward since even teacher praise amounts to this. The question then is one of the nature of the reward rather than the presence or absence of it.

RESEARCH

Joyce, B. R. (1991). Common misconceptions about co-operative learning and gifted students: response to Allan. *Educational Leadership*, **48**(March), 72-74.

Slavin, R. E. (1988-89). Research on co-operative learning: consensus and controversy. *Educational Leadership*, **47**(December-January), 52-54.

Webb, N. M. (1991). Task-related verbal interaction and mathematics learning in small groups. *Journal for Research in Mathematics Education*, **22**(5), 366-389.

The benefits of small group work depend on the type of grouping

The benefits of small group work appear to be most marked when there is an appreciable, but not the full range of abilities in the group. In mixed-sex groups, the achievement of males and females is most similar when there is an equal number of males and females.

A substantial body of research on small group learning suggests that there are benefits for pupils of all ages in all subject areas across a wide range of tasks. A common misconception about small group work is that it implies or requires groups that are mixed in terms of ability, ethnicity, gender, and social class. However it seems that the positive effects of small group activity may not be the same for all pupils and that the composition of the group affects the benefits.

In summary, the research suggests that the optimum grouping would comprise:

- 'near' mixed ability groups: high- and middle-attainers or middle- and low-attainers
- in mixed-sex groups, balanced numbers of boys and girls.

The reasons for these suggestions are explored below.

Effects of ability grouping

Research into small group work has consistently found that:

- pupils giving help and explanations, and
- pupils seeking and getting help from their peers

both lead to gains in attainment for those pupils.

There is substantial evidence that the extent to which a pupil gives detailed explanations is a good predictor of how much that pupil will benefit from small-group working. Not surprisingly, it is the higher-achieving pupils that do more explaining when working in a mixed-ability group and so gain most. In mixed-ability groups it is the lower-attaining pupils who ask the most questions. Hence in groups with a wide spread of attainment, the middle-attainers miss out, as they neither seek nor give help. In groups with a narrow range of attainment, pupils appear to be discouraged from either asking for, or giving, help.

In addition, the type of grouping may affect the sort of intervention provided by the teacher. Lower-attaining pupils who are grouped together within mixed-ability classrooms appear to receive less appropriate teaching than high-attainers and benefit least from this type of close-ability grouping in mixed-ability classes.

It seems then that the most appropriate form of grouping is 'near' mixed ability groups. This maximises the potential for everyone to be involved in giving or receiving explanations. For example, the middle-attainers seek explanations when grouped with high-attainers and give explanations when grouped with lower-attainers.

Effect of gender balance

As indicated above, the research on small group work has consistently found that pupils giving and receiving help are positively related to achievement. Conversely, it seems that asking for explanations and getting an inadequate or no response at all has a negative effect on achievement.

This latter finding is particularly pertinent for examining the experiences of males and females working together. One study that looked in detail at the interactions between male and female pupils working in small groups of four found that:

- male pupils received more explanations, both from peers and from the teacher, than the female pupils did
- female pupils were more likely than males not to get answers or explanations in response to requests or questions.

Males therefore experienced most of the interactions beneficial for achievement: seeking and receiving help. On the other hand, females received most of the interactions *detrimental* for achievement: getting inadequate or no responses.

However, these different gender experiences were also dependent on the composition of the group in terms of the balance of males and females. Examining the patterns of interaction within groups of four pupils, the same research established that:

- females were more responsive to requests for help than males
- males responded more to other males than to females
- in groups of three females and one male the females directed more attention to the male than might be expected given the group composition
- in groups with a majority of males, the males tended to focus their attention on the other males
- the disparity of experience between males and females was least in equally balanced groups.

Perhaps not surprisingly, therefore, the research found that the achievement of males and females was most similar in balanced groups, although this research did not examine single-sex groups.

RESEARCH

Slavin, R.E., Madden, N.A. and Leavey, M. Effects of co-operative learning and individualized instruction on mainstreamed students. *Exceptional Children*, 1984. 50(5), 434-448.

Webb, N.M. (1984). Sex differences in interaction and achievement in co-operative small groups. *Journal of Educational Psychology*, 76(1) 33-44.

Webb, N.M. (1989). Peer interaction and learning in small groups. *International Journal of Educational Research*, 13(1) 21-39.

Mathematical attainment grouping can lead to some gains in attainment

Contrary to popular belief, setting does not appear to lead necessarily to low self-esteem for low-attainers. It would appear that seeing someone of similar attainment cope is more motivating than seeing mastery.

Attainment grouping - general findings

Considering the importance of the issue, it is surprising how little systematic research has been undertaken in this country into the relative effectiveness of mixed-attainment and homogenous-attainment class groupings (or 'sets').

There is little evidence in the research that much is gained from grouping by general attainment, but grouping by attainment in mathematics, either within or across classes, can result in small gains for all pupils. However, it is important to note that organising several different 'ability-groups' within the same class places a severe burden on the teacher's administrative and managerial skills. For example, several studies have found that when dealing with three separate groups working on different materials, teachers spend as much as half the available lesson time on administrative matters, so that the amount of teacher input received by each group can be as little as one-sixth of that experienced in 'whole-class' teaching.

Where students are working co-operatively (see previous pages), this may not be so much of a problem, but where the pupils are dependent on the teacher's input in order to progress, then within-class grouping is likely to have a deleterious effect on pupil attainment.

Since there is little evidence to suggest pupils are academically harmed by attainment-grouping, and any gains are relatively small for most pupils, the issue may be to what extent attitudes are affected. The research suggests that:

- attainment grouping improves pupils' attitudes towards subject, but does not affect attitude towards school
- any effects on self-esteem are small: positive for low-attainers and slightly negative for others.

Attainment grouping - effects on high attainers

A review of research (concentrating on research in the USA) which examined the effect of different teaching approaches on high-attainers when pupils are grouped by attainment, found three types of study:

- Where pupils of all levels of attainment were grouped by attainment and taught with similar materials in similar ways. Here the effects are small (but positive)–in the region of an achievement gain of one month in attainment for high-attainers.
- Where teaching material was adjusted to needs of a particular group (ie an 'enrichment' or 'extension' approach). The effects were larger– 4 months' gain for high attainers–although, since these groups were given special attention by teachers who had received additional training, it may well be that all pupils (whatever their ability) would have benefited from such a programme.
- Where the curriculum was 'rewritten from scratch' for the high-attainers (ie an 'acceleration' approach), the high-achievers experienced gains of up to a whole year.

All these studies found that 'setting' improved average achievement levels for pupils. However, in most cases, this was because gains made by higher-attaining students more than offset losses for lower-attainers. This raises the question of whether this was just an artefact of the way in which achievement was measured. An easier test would allow less 'headroom' for the most able, so that their scores would be relatively compressed, while allowing for greater differentiation between lower-attainers. In this case the decrease in scores for lower-attainers could more than offset the increase for the higher-attainers, leading to an apparent net *decrease* in overall levels of achievement.

Furthermore, while some research supports the idea that gifted pupils and high-attainers do benefit from some attainment grouping (particularly where learning materials are tailored to the pupils' capabilities), it is not clear whether the benefits are caused by the grouping or by the provision of differentiated learning materials.

Research also shows that high-attainers gain from mixed-ability collaborative work as much as any other pupils. The question is therefore, whether 'setting' would produce any *additional* gains for higher-attainers, over and above that which would be produced by the provision of differentiated work together with collaborative learning.

If ability in mathematics is not a fixed entity, as many researchers suggest, then grouping by attainment may mean that particular expectations are set up from which pupils will have great difficulty breaking free.

RESEARCH

Allan, S.D., Ability-grouping research reviews: what do they say about grouping and the gifted? *Educational Leadership,* 1991. **48**(March), 60-65.

Slavin, R.E., Are co-operative learning and "untracking" harmful to the gifted? Response to Allan. *Educational Leadership,* 1991. **48**(March), 68-71.

Many aspects of mathematics teaching are under-researched

Although this review has attempted to cover the important findings from research in mathematics education, it is perhaps just as important to identify those areas where answers are most needed, but where the research evidence is weak.

The nature of the learner

One of the strongest messages that comes from the research literature is that the knowledge that pupils acquire is strongly tied to the particular context and situation in which it was learnt, unless careful steps are taken to avoid this. However, it is not the case that everything needs to be learnt 'from scratch' to be applied in different contexts. A major issue for future research, then, is: how can teaching be designed so as to maximise the 'transferability' of the learning to new and unfamiliar contexts, or what should the curriculum be like if transfer is as difficult as it appears to be? This will include how to choose and exploit contexts for teaching so as to facilitate the transfer from 'concrete' to 'formal' mathematics.

It is also clear that pupils 'make sense' of the mathematics that they have been taught in unpredictable ways, but, as noted earlier, addressing the most common misconceptions during teaching can improve pupil achievement. In science, the nature of common misconceptions is quite well catalogued in a form accessible to teachers, but no such comparable resource exists for mathematics teachers. A systematic programme of the identification and cataloguing of the different ways in which students develop their mathematical competences, together with the common misconceptions developed along the way, and teaching strategies that can be used either to avoid or address them, would appear to be a very important step in raising standards of achievement in mathematics.

Teaching mathematics

Most research into teacher effectiveness up to the present has concentrated on identifying differences between 'expert' and 'novice' teachers. This research has resulted in a reasonably clear understanding of the differences between 'expert' and 'novice' teachers, but very little light has been shed on how a 'novice' teacher might become 'expert', possibly because the differences between 'experts' and novices are described in terms of surface features. For example, it is clear that expert teachers have much smoother transitions between different phases of the lesson than do novices, but it is far from clear whether this is a cause or an effect of expertise (telling a teacher to 'have smoother transitions' may be no more helpful than advising an unsuccessful clown to 'be funnier'). Although identifying characteristics of 'good' teachers is an important first step, in the future it seems much more important to focus research on the strategies which might be offered to teachers to affect their practices.

Classroom management and organisation

The research reviewed in this booklet establishes clearly that collaborative learning enhances achievement, and that a great deal is known about the conditions under which learning is optimised. Organising effective group-work does, however, place considerable demands on teachers' classroom management skills: for most teachers, the more groups there are in the classroom, the less time the teacher spends teaching, and the more time the teacher spends organising. However, teaching the whole class effectively as a single group is extremely difficult if there is a wide range of attainment within the class. For this reason, many secondary schools choose to organise pupils into classes that appear to be more or less homogenous in mathematical attainment.

Teaching mathematics in homogenous-ability classes does, in general, appear to raise the attainment of the highest-achieving pupils, but this is frequently at the expense of other pupils. The research shows that homogenous ability 'setting' need not lead to negative attitudes towards mathematics amongst those in the 'lower' sets, although the experience of many teachers is that it often does so. An important organisational issue for mathematics teaching would therefore appear to be to ascertain under what conditions homogenous ability grouping can raise achievement standards without producing a worsening of pupil attitudes towards mathematics. It is also clear that while the achievement of girls of median attainment has caught up with and overtaken that of boys, girls are still significantly under-represented at the highest levels of achievement. Identifying and addressing the cause of this underachievement is an important priority for future research.

Curriculum development

There have been many exciting and innovative curriculum developments in mathematics during the 1980s and early 1990s. At the primary level, the PrIME project and associated CAN (Calculator Aware Number) curriculum explored the possibilities for using calculators to teach number. From the mid-1980s on, a variety of graded assessment projects were launched, all of which were developed in close collaboration with practising teachers, and were implemented on a large scale. Another notable large-scale curriculum development project was the 'Better Schools' project based at the West Sussex Institute of Higher Education.

It is clear that these projects did impact on teachers and curricula, but, unfortunately, even where careful evaluations were carried out these were not reported in 'refereed journals', subject to peer review. In this sense, then, accumulated knowledge and experience is not available to be passed on and every new project 'reinvents the wheel'. Properly planned and funded evaluations should be a feature of curriculum developments in the future so that succeeding curriculum developments can build on the strengths and address the weaknesses of previous innovations. A good example would be the need for long-term study of the effects of using calculators.

NOTES

Page 1: Introduction

¶1 "As part of its work ... published in three volumes in 1983." The three volumes were:

Bell, A. W.; Costello, J. & Kühemann, D. (1983). *A review of research in mathematical education part A: research on learning and teaching*. Windsor: NFER Nelson.

Nickson, M. & Bishop, A. (1983). *A review of research in mathematical education part B.* Windsor: NFER Nelson.

Howson, A. G. (1983). *A review of research in mathematical education part C: curriculum development and curriculum research: a historical and comparative view.* Windsor: NFER Nelson.

Page 4: The international context

¶1 Except where otherwise indicated, the findings reported here are all from Robitaille, D. F. & Garden, R. A. (Eds.). (1988). *The IEA study of mathematics II: contexts and outcomes of school mathematics.* Oxford: Pergamon, but are cross-validated by, and broadly consistent with the IEAP research reported in Lapointe, A. E.; Mead, N. A. & Askew, J. M. (1992). *Learning mathematics: report of the second International Assessment of Educational Progress.* Princeton, NJ: Educational Testing Service Center for the Assessment of Educational Progress.

¶5 "However, in number and algebra, in almost all countries, pupil performance fell far short of teachers' expectation." Teachers were asked, for each item, whether they had taught the topic to a sufficient degree for the pupils to be able to answer the item. The actual results were relatively close to the predictions in geometry and statistics, but much lower in algebra and number.

¶5 "There is also a suggestion ... than it is at age 13." A regression of attainment from the IAEP survey (Lapointe *et al, op cit*) shows that, in England, achievement at age 13 is above that which would be predicted at age 9, which is consistent with OFSTED findings that the achievement of students in number in year 3 gives particular cause for concern *(The teaching and learning of number in primary schools, HMSO, 1993).*

¶7 "Nevertheless, one conclusion that seems to emerge ... shorter lessons." For example, a multiple regression of arithmetic scores (excluding one extreme outlier) at age 14 on five 'context' variables (proportion of the school timetable devoted to mathematics at ages 14 and 18, the proportion of teachers of 14- and 18-year-olds fully qualified in mathematics, and the length of a typical lesson) explained over 98% of the variance in national average arithmetic scores [analysis based on Robitaille & Garden *op cit* pp 36, 48 and 105]. It is also worth noting that total time spent on mathematics (eg in terms of number of hours of mathematics per year) did *not* seem to have any influence on pupil achievement.

¶8 "However, the countries ... most negative attitudes to the subject." The IEA study found a correlation of -0.7 between achievement in number at age 14 and pupils' liking for the subject (Robitaille & Garden *op cit*, pp 105 and 185). However, it is also worth noting that the IAEP study (Lapointe, Mead & Askew *op cit*) found *no* significant relationship between attitude and achievement.

Page 6: Young children's competency with number is often underestimated

¶2 "Count meaningfully": Baroody, A. J. & White, M. S. (1983). The development of counting skills and number conservation. *Child Study Journal,* **13**, 95-105 and Young-Loveridge, J. M. (1987). Learning mathematics. *British Journal of Developmental Psychology,* **5**(2), 155-167.

¶2 "Have some understanding of addition and subtraction with small numbers": Baroody, A. J. (1987). The development of counting strategies for single-digit addition. *Journal for Research in Mathematics Education,* **18**(2), 141-157.

¶2 "Invent strategies for solving problems": Leder, G. C. (1989). Number concepts of pre-school children. *Perceptual and Motor Skills,* **69**, 1048-1050 and Groen, G. T. & Resnick, L. B. (1977). Can preschoolers invent addition algorithms? *Journal of Educational Psychology,* **69**(6), 645-652.

¶3 "Detailed interviews ... to find out the quantity." Munn, P. (1994). The early development of literacy and numeracy skills. *European Early Childhood Education Research Journal,* **2**(1), 5-18 p16.

¶6 "This study also ... the 'decade' system": Munn *op cit.*

¶6 "idiosyncratic number names": the naming of numbers between ten and twenty is much more regular in most other languages, and is particularly simple in, for example, Chinese, Korean and Welsh.

¶7 "Another study of a small class ... by the time they enter 'Reception' classes": Aubrey, C. (1994). An investigation of children's knowledge of mathematics at school entry and the knowledge their teachers hold about teaching and learning mathematics, about young learners, and mathematical subject knowledge. *British Educational Research Journal,* **20**(1), 105-120.

Page 8: 'Knowing by heart' and 'figuring out' support each other in pupils' progression in number

"To accept without question ... will grow even wider." Gray, E. M. (1991). An analysis of diverging approaches to simple arithmetic: preference and its consequences. *Educational Studies in Mathematics,* **22**(6), 551-574.

¶1 "There is strong evidence ... multiplication." Hart, K. M. (Ed.) (1981). *Children's understanding of mathematics: 11-16.* London: John Murray.

¶2 "A study of arithmetical methods ...": Gray *op cit.*

¶4 "These findings are supported ... and anticipate solution strategies." Steffe, L. P. (1983). Children's algorithms as schemes. *Educational Studies in Mathematics,* **14**(2), 109-125. The distinction that Steffe makes is not quite the same as Gray's, referring instead to 'deduction' or 'memorised procedures'.

Page 10: Moving from practical to formal work is often far from straightforward

¶1 "Research demonstrates ... in an abstract form." Hughes, M. (1986). *Children and number: difficulties in learning mathematics.* Oxford: Basil Blackwell.

¶2 "Children's Mathematical Frameworks project": Johnson, D. C. (Ed.) (1989). *Children's mathematical frameworks 8-13: a study of classroom teaching.* Windsor: NFER-Nelson.

¶6 "Similarly, a detailed study ... rather than the pupils' own discoveries." Walkerdine, V. (1988). *The mastery of reason: cognitive development and the production of rationality.* London: Routledge.

¶8 "although asking students to write about what they have learnt can provide very revealing insights." See for example, Miller, L. D. (1992). Teacher benefits from using impromptu writing prompts in algebra classes. *Journal for Research in Mathematics Education*, **23**(4), 329-340.

Page 12: Learning is more effective when common misconceptions are addressed in teaching

¶1 "One of the most important findings ... patterns that they see around them." See, for example, the publications arising from the Strategies in Secondary Mathematics and Science (SESM) project:

Hart, K. M. (1984). *Ratio: children's strategies and errors.* Windsor: NFER-Nelson.

Booth, L. R. (1984). *Algebra: children's strategies and errors.* Windsor: NFER-Nelson.

Kerslake, D. (1986). *Fractions: children's strategies and errors.* Windsor: NFER-Nelson.

¶3 "This can be counter-productive ... with more complex examples": Bell, A W (1984). Structures, contexts and learning. *Journal of Structural Learning*, **8**(2), 165-171.

¶6 "In the Diagnostic Teaching project ... ": Bell, A W (1993). Some experiments in diagnostic teaching. *Educational Studies in Mathematics*, **24**(1), 115-137.

Page 14: Careful choice of examples improves children's concept formation

¶3 "Experiments conducted ... a mixture of examples (ruling in) and non-examples (ruling out)." Erickson, J. R. & Jones, M. R. (1978). Thinking. *Annual Review of Psychology*, **29**, 61-90.

¶4 "However, researchers in mathematics classrooms ... than sequences of examples alone." Shumway, R. J.; White, A. L.; Wilson, P. & Brombacher, B. (1983). Feature frequency and negative instances in concept learning. *American Educational Research Journal*, **20**(3), 451-459

¶5 "In the psychological studies... (ie they do not learn to rule in)": Wilson, P. S. (1986). Feature frequency and the use of negative instances in a geometric task. *Journal for Research in Mathematics Education*, **17**(2), 130-139.

¶8 "There is also evidence that ... random sequencing": Petty, O. S. & Jansson, L. C. (1987). Sequencing examples and non-examples to facilitate concept attainment. *Journal for Research in Mathematics Education*, **18**(2), 112-125.

Page 16: Effective questioning can raise achievement

¶1 The terms 'lower-level' and 'higher-level' derive from the levels of B. S. Bloom's *Taxonomy of Educational Objectives*, New York: Longman, 1956.

¶3 "Although many inquiries ... mainly to recall or recognise". Redfield, D. T. & Rousseau, E. W. (1981). A meta-analysis of experimental research on teacher questioning behaviour. *Review of Educational Research*, **51**(2), 237-245.

¶3 Subsequent analyses of the same, and similar data have cast doubt on the efficacy of 'higher-level' questions. However, since the biggest differences in pupil learning tend to be shown in the smaller studies (where researchers verified that teachers were actually using higher-level questions rather than assuming that they would after being trained to), there is reasonable support for the assertion that asking more demanding questions does produce better learning.

¶4 "teachers can increase the proportion of higher-level questions that they use": Galloway, C. G. & Mickelson, N. I. (1973). Improving teachers' questions. *Elementary School Journal*, **74**(3), 145-148.

¶4 "such changes are accompanied... pupil performance"; see for example: Burton, J. K.; Niles, J. A.; Lalik, R. M. & Reed, W. M. (1986). Cognitive capacity engagement during and following interspersed mathemagenic questions. *Journal of Educational Psychology*, **78**(2), 147-152, and Otto, P. B. & Schuck, R. F. (1983). The effect of a teacher questioning strategy training program on teaching behavior, pupil achievement, and retention. *Journal of Research in Science Teaching*, **20**(6), 521-528.

¶4 "Further these effects are more pronounced ... than for simple recall of facts": Hamilton, R. J. (1985). A framework for the evaluation of the effectiveness of adjunct questions and objectives. *Review of Educational Research*, **55**(1), 47-85.

¶7 "although other studies suggest that increasing wait-time is only beneficial for higher-level questions": Riley, J. P. (1986). The effects of teachers' wait-time and knowledge comprehension questioning on science achievement. *Journal of Research in Science Teaching*, **23**(4), 335-342.

¶8 "However, what is rather surprising ... *reduction* in pupil achievement in mathematics": Tobin, K. (1986). Effects of teacher wait time on discourse characteristics in mathematics and language arts classes. *American Educational Research Journal*, **23**(2), 191-200.

Page 18: The quality of praise is at least as important as its quantity

¶1 "teachers regarded as more effective than average actually used less praise than their less successful colleagues": see, for example, Good, T. L. & Grouws, D. A. (1975). *Process-product relationships in fourth grade mathematics classrooms.* Final report No. NE-G-00-0-0123. Unpublished report prepared for National Institute of Education. Columbia, MO: University of Missouri.

¶2 "What appears to be most important for praise to be effective is that it is contingent, ... specific, ... and credible": O'Leary, K. & O'Leary, S. (Eds.). (1977). *Classroom management: the successful use of behaviour modification.* New York, NY: Pergamon.

Page 20: Pupils achieve more in mathematics when their teachers know their levels of achievement and can act on this information

¶2 "For example, in a regional initiative ... by 30%": Grisay, A. (1991). Improving assessment in primary schools. In P. Weston (Ed.) *Assessment of pupil achievement* (pp. 103-119). Amsterdam, Holland: Swets & Zeitlinger.

¶2 "On the other hand, ... on the quality of teaching." Herman, J. L. (1992). What research tells us about good assessment. *Educational Leadership*, **49**(8), 74-78.

¶3 "This research ... little additional effect": Bangert-Drowns, R. L.; Kulik, J A & Kulik, C.-L. C. (1991). Effects of frequent classroom testing. *Journal of Educational Research*, **85**(2), 89-99.

¶4 "What *is* clear ... mathematical concepts." Hoge, R. D. & Coladarci, T. (1989). Teacher-based judgments of academic achievement: a review of literature. *Review of Educational Research*, **59**(3), 297-313.

¶5 "However, knowing a pupil's general level of attainment ... before 'moving on'": Denvir, B. & Brown, M. L. (1986). Understanding of number concepts in low-attaining 7-9 year olds: parts 1 and 2. *Educational Studies in Mathematics*, **17**, 15-36 and 143-164.

¶6 "It is also clear that ... in number fact knowledge, understanding, problem solving, and confidence." Carpenter, T. P.; Fennema, E.; Peterson, P. L.; Chiang, C. P. & Loef, M. (1989). Using knowledge of children's mathematics thinking in classroom teaching: an experimental study. *American Educational Research Journal*, **26**(4), 499-531.

¶7 "In addition, ... observe their pupils' solutions." Peterson, P. L.; Carpenter, T. & Fennema, E. (1989). Teachers' knowledge of pupils' knowledge in mathematics problem solving: correlational and case analyses. *Journal of Educational Psychology*, **81**(4), 558-569.

¶8 "However, by itself... wide range of teaching approaches." Helmke, A. & Schrader, F. W. (1987). Interactional effects of instructional quality and teacher judgement accuracy on achievement. *Teaching and Teacher Education*, **3**(2), 91-98.

Page 22: Pupils need to be introduced to a wide range of problem-solving situations

¶2 "Further distinctions are possible..."This classification is based on the work of Charles, R.I. & Lester, F. (1982) *Teaching problem solving - what, why and how*. Palo Alto, CA: Dale Seymour Publications

¶3 "One review of research ... non-standard problems". Hembree, R. (1992). Experiments and relational studies in problem solving: a meta-analysis. *Journal for Research in Mathematics Education*, **23**(3), 242-273.

¶4 "One such study suggests that ...": Peterson, P. L.; Fennema, E. & Carpenter, T. P. (1988/1989). Using knowledge of how students think about mathematics. *Educational Leadership*, **46**(4), 42-46.

Page 24: Success in problem-solving requires both specific content knowledge and general skills

¶2 "A study of primary school pupils ... without coming off": Karmiloff-Smith, A. (1979). Problem-solving construction and representations of closed railway circuits. *Archives of Psychology*, **57**(1), 37-59.

¶3 "More generally, ... while novices focus on surface details." Nickerson, R. S. (1988). On improving thinking through instruction. In E. Z. Rothkopf (Ed.) *Review of research in education* (pp. 3-57). Washington, DC: American Educational Research Association.

¶5 "However, by and large, such attempts have been unsuccessful." A notable exception to this has been the Cognitive Acceleration in Science Project, which found that a total of 30 one-hour 'thinking skill' lessons, administered once a fortnight during the first two years of secondary school, improved the performance of pupils at GCSE in science and *mathematics and English* by about half a grade (see Adey, P. S. & Shayer, M. (1993). An exploration of long-term far-transfer effects following an extended intervention program in the high school science curriculum. *Cognition and Instruction*, **11**(1), 1-29.

¶6 "Nevertheless, ... particularly with low-attaining pupils": see, for example, Cardelle, E. M. (1992). Effects of teaching metacognitive skills to pupils with low mathematics ability. *Teaching and Teacher Education*, **8**(2), 109-121.

Page 26: What mathematics is learnt is closely tied to the circumstances in which it is learnt

¶1 "Children working in Brazilian ... in formal tests." Carraher, T. N.; Carraher, D. W. & Schliemann, A. D. (1990). Mathematics in the streets and in schools. In V. Lee (Ed.) *Children's Learning in School* (pp. 91-102). London, UK: Hodder & Stoughton in association with The Open University.

¶1 "A study of adults ... while shopping." Lave, J. (1988). *Cognition in practice: mind, mathematics and culture in everyday life.* Cambridge: Cambridge University Press.

¶4 "Rather than trying ... and the culture of the classroom." Brown, J. S.; Collins, A. & Duguid, P. (1989). Situated cognition and the culture of learning. *Educational Researcher*, **18**(1), 32-42.

Page 28: Pupils' self-confidence and beliefs affect their success in mathematics

¶1 "The way that teachers praise and criticise pupils ... ": Diener, C. I. & Dweck, C. S. (1978). An analysis of learned helplessness: continuous change in performance strategy and achievement cognitions following failure. *Journal of Personality and Social Psychology*, **36**(5), 451-462.

¶1 Attribution theory classifies the way that pupils attribute success and failure along four dimensions:

- Locus–whether the cause of success or failure resides within the individual or is due to external factors. For example, the amount of ability or amount of effort are within the pupil, whereas the difficulty of the task or the amount of help available are external factors.

- Stability over time–whether the cause is perceived by the pupil as being fixed forever, or alterable in the future. The more stable an attribute the more influence it has.

- Controllability–whether the cause is perceived as being under the control of the individual, for example effort, or outside their control, for example ability.

- Specificity–whether the cause is seen as applying only to particular experiences, or whether it is regarded as extending to all undertakings.

¶2 "Pupils who view ability in mathematics as fixed ...": Dweck, C. S. (1986). Motivational processes affecting learning. *American Psychologist* **41**(10), 1040-1048.

¶4 "A study of five classes ...": Cobb, P.; Yackel, E. & Wood, T. (1992). Interaction and learning in mathematics classroom situations. *Educational Studies in Mathematics*, **23**(1), 99-122.

¶6 "More generally ... becomes optional." Kloosterman, P. (1988). Self-confidence and motivation in mathematics. *Journal of Educational Psychology*, **80**(3), 345-351.

Page 30: Calculators can improve both performance and attitude

¶1 "One review examined 79 reports of investigations ...": Hembree, R. and Dessart. R.J. (1986). Effects of hand-held calculators in precollege mathematics education: A meta-analysis. *Journal for Research in Mathematics Education*, **17**(2), 83-99.

¶3 "An update of this review ...": Hembree, R. and Dessart, D.J. (1992) Research on calculators in mathematics education, in J.T. Fey and C.R. Hirsch (Eds.), *Calculators in mathematics education (1992 yearbook* (pp23-32). Reston, VA: National Council of Teachers of Mathematics

¶5 "The Calculator Aware Number (CAN) Curriculum ...": Shuard, H.; Walsh, A.; Goodwin, J. & Worcester, V. (1991). *Calculators, children and mathematics: the calculator-aware number curriculum.* London: Simon & Schuster.

¶7 "new ways of exploiting the calculator as a tool for *teaching* number": see for example Groves, S (1994, April), *Calculators: a learning environment to promote number sense.* Paper presented at Annual meeting of the American Educational Research Association held at New Orleans, LA.

¶8 "Although early experiments focused on older pupils": see, for example, Ruthven, K. (1990). The influence of graphic calculator use on translation from graphic to symbolic forms. *Educational Studies in Mathematics*, **21**, 431-450.

¶8 "the use of graphical calculators can enhance both attainment and attitudes with lower-secondary pupils": see for example Smart, T. (1995). Visualisation, confidence and magic: the role of the graphics calculator. In L. Burton & B. Jaworski (Eds.), *Technology: a bridge between teaching and learning mathematics* Bromley, UK: Chartwell-Bratt.

Page 32: The differences between girls' and boys' attainment in mathematics are small and narrowing

¶2 "the achievement of boys and girls was comparable at age 11": Foxman, D. D.; Cresswell, M. J.; Ward, M.; Badger, M. E.; Tuson, J. A. & Bloomfield, B. A. (1980). *Mathematical development: primary survey report no 1.* London: Her Majesty's Stationery Office., p71.

¶2 "the average scores for boys at 15 were higher than those for girls in all fifteen topics tested (significantly so in 12 of them)": Foxman, *et al*, *op cit* p76.

¶3 "The format of the items": see for example: Murphy, R. J. L. (1982). Sex differences in objective test performance. *British Journal of Educational Psychology*, **52**, 213-19.

¶3 "the contexts used": see for example Graf, R. G. & Riddell, J. C. (1972). Sex-differences in problem-solving as a function of problem context. *Journal of Educational Research*, **65**, 451-2.

¶4 "The 1992 pilot of national curriculum tests for 14-year olds ... with only 60% of boys)": Department for Education (1992). *Testing 14 year olds in 1992: results of the National Curriculum assessments in England.* London: Department for Education, pp6-7.

¶4 "Compared with the levels of achievement reported in the Cockcroft report for 1979": Committee of Inquiry into the Teaching of Mathematics in Schools (1982). *Report: mathematics counts.* London: Her Majesty's Stationery Office, p250.

¶4 "this improvement in girls' performance ... an extra 6 months mathematics learning." Inevitably reporting complex data in such a simplistic way requires a large number of assumptions. This estimate was derived by assuming that the spread of attainment in the cohort increases with age, as described in Wiliam, D. (1992). Special needs and the distribution of attainment in the national curriculum. *British Journal of Educational Psychology*, **62**, 397-403.

¶5 "However, this improvement ... good grades in Mathematics": Stobart, G.; Elwood, J. & Quinlan, M. (1992). Gender bias in examinations: how equal are the opportunities? *British Educational Research Journal*, **18**(3), 261-276.

¶5 "and at the highest levels ... two girls to every three boys." Department for Education (1994). *Testing 14 year olds in 1994: results of the National Curriculum assessments in England.* London: Department for Education and School Curriculum and Assessment Authority (1994). *GCSE examinations results 1993.* London: School Curriculum and Assessment Authority.

¶6 All the data in this paragraph are taken from Sanders, N.; Read, R. & Tarsh, J. (1994). *Science and maths: a consultation paper on the supply and demand of newly qualified young people.* London: Department for Education.

¶7 "Many reasons have been proposed ... less helpful in learning mathematics." see, for example, chapters 1, 2, 3, 7 and 8 in McGuinness, D. (1985). *When children don't learn : understanding the biology and psychology of learning disabilities.* New York: Basic Books.

Page 34: Computers can have a substantial positive impact on pupils' achievement in mathematics

¶1 "the pattern of usage is still very varied and very sparse": Watson, D. M. (Ed.) (1993). The ImpacT report: *an evaluation of the impact of information technology on children's achievements in primary and secondary schools.* London: King's College London Centre for Educational Studies.

¶2 "The classroom-based studies ... low-attainers": Kulik, J. A. & Kulik, C.-L. C. (1989). Effectiveness of computer-based instruction. *School Library Media Quarterly*, **17**(3), 156-159.

¶2 "there is little evidence to support the notion that teaching programming ... improves general mathematical skills": see, for example, Eubanks, C. L. (1988). A comparison of the performance on the New York State Regents Competency Test in Mathematics of remedial high school pupils receiving computer-assisted instruction and pupils not receiving computer-assisted instruction. *Graduate Research in Urban Education and Related Disciplines*, **19**(1-2), 52-66 and Turner, S. V. & Land, M. L. (1988). Cognitive effects of a Logo-enriched mathematics program for middle school pupils. *Journal of Educational Computing Research*, **4**(4), 443-452.

¶2 "the use of paper- or card-based games have been just as effective": see for example, Fuson, K. C. & Brinko, K. T. (1985). The comparative effectiveness of microcomputers and flash cards in the drill and practice of basic mathematics facts. *Journal for Research in Mathematics Education*, **16**(3), 225-232.

¶5 "The crucial feature ... small-group and individualised teaching." Kaput, J. J. (1992). Technology and mathematics education. In D. A. Grouws (Ed.) *Handbook of research on mathematics teaching and learning* (pp. 515-556). New York: Macmillan.

¶6 "Another effective example ... one lesson of Logo per week": Harel, I. (1990). Children as software designers: a constructionist approach for learning mathematics. *Journal of Mathematical Behavior*, **9**(1), 3-93 (whole issue).

¶8 "Pupils in economically disadvantaged areas, those from ethnic minorities, and females have less access to computers both at school and at home." Sutton, R. E. (1991). Equity and computers in the schools: a decade of research. *Review of Educational Research*, **61**(4), 475-503.

¶8 "significant *potential* for remedying inequality": see for example, Noss, R. (1987). Children's learning of geometrical concepts through Logo. *Journal for Research in Mathematics Education*, **18**(5), 343-362.

Page 36: Co-operative small group work has positive effects on pupil achievement

"The benefits of co-operative learning activities hold for pupils at all age levels, for all subject areas, and for a wide range of tasks, such as those involving rote-decoding, retention, and memory skills, as well as problem-solving ability.": Bossert, S. T. (1988). Co-operative activities in the classroom. In E. Z. Rothkopf (Ed.) *Review of research in education* (pp. 225-250). Washington, DC: American Educational Research Association (p 225).

¶1 "There is general consensus ... attainment of the goal": Slavin, R. E. (1988-89). Research on co-operative learning: consensus and controversy. *Educational Leadership*, **47**(December-January), 52-54.

Page 38: The benefits of small group work depend on the type of grouping

¶1 "A substantial body of research ...": see for example Slavin, R. E.; Madden, N. A. & Leavey, M. (1984). Effects of co-operative learning and individualised learning on mainstreamed students. *Exceptional Children*, **50**(5), 434-448.

¶4 "Not surprisingly ... and so gain most.": Peterson, P. L.; Janicki, T. C. & Swing, S. R. (1981). Ability/treatment interaction effects on children's learning in large-group and small-group approaches. *American Educational Research Journal*, **18**, 452-474.

¶5 "Lower-attaining pupils ... benefit least from this type of close-ability grouping": Wilkinson, L. C. (1988). Grouping children for learning: implications for kindergarten education. In E. Z. Rothkopf (Ed.) *Review of research in education* (pp. 203-223). Washington, DC: American Educational Research Association.

¶8 "One study that looked in detail... requests or questions": Webb, N. M. (1984). Sex differences in interaction and achievement in cooperative small groups. *Journal of Educational Psychology*, **76**(1), 33-44.

Page 40: Mathematical attainment grouping can lead to some gains in attainment

¶2 "For example, several studies have found that when dealing with three separate groups ... in 'whole-class' teaching": see for example Good, T. L.; Grouws, D. A.; Mason, D. A.; Slavings, R. L. & Cramer, K. (1990). An observational study of small-group mathematics instruction in elementary schools. *American Educational Research Journal*, **27**(4), 755-782.

¶4 "attainment grouping improves ... slightly negative for others.": Allan, S. D. (1991). Ability-grouping research reviews: what do they say about grouping and the gifted? *Educational Leadership*, **48**(March), 60-65 and Slavin, R. E. (1991). Are cooperative learning and "untracking" harmful to the gifted? Response to Allan. *Educational Leadership*, **48**(March), 68-71.

¶5 "A review of research ... up to a whole year": Kulik, J. A. & Kulik, C.-L. C. (1984). Effects of accelerated instruction on pupils. *Review of Educational Research*, **54**(3), 409-425.

Page 42: Many aspects of mathematics teaching are under-researched

¶3 "In science, ... no such comparable resource exists for mathematics teachers." See for example, Driver, R. H.; Squires, A.; Rushworth, P. & Wood-Robinson, V. (1994). *Making sense of secondary science: research into children's ideas*. London: Routledge.

¶5 "Organising effective group-work ... the more time the teacher spends organising." This is clearly not true for all teachers, but it does appear that teachers who can generate as much 'quality teaching time' with many small groups as with whole classes are the exception rather than the rule.

¶8 For a discussion of the constraints of evaluation in three Government-funded projects (the Technical and Vocational Education Initiative, the Low-Attaining Pupils Programme, and TVEI-related In-service Training) see Hutchinson, B.; Hopkins, D. & Howard, J. (1988). The problem of validity in the qualitative evaluation of categorically funded curriculum development projects. *Educational Research*, **30**(1), 54-64.

¶7 "From the mid-1980s on, ... and were implemented on a large scale." These included the Oxford Certificate of Educational Achievement (OCEA), Graded Assessment in Mathematics (GAIM) and the Shell Centre's Numeracy projects.

Printed in the United Kingdom for HMSO
Dd. 300294 C50 5/95 3400/3 13110